W9-BYY-821

matrix
methods
in
accounting

john k. shank

MATRIX
METHODS IN ACCOUNTING

MATRIX
METHODS IN ACCOUNTING

JOHN K. SHANK
Harvard University

ADDISON-WESLEY PUBLISHING COMPANY

Reading, Massachusetts • Menlo Park, California • London • Don Mills, Ontario

This book is in the
ADDISON-WESLEY PAPERBACK SERIES IN ACCOUNTING

William J. Bruns, Jr.
Consulting Editor

EDITOR'S FOREWORD

The pace of technological and social change in recent years has created difficult problems for accounting and accountants. Data processing and information technology have provided new tools. Quantitative methods and behavioral sciences have suggested that new methods of solving accounting problems may be appropriate. The dependence upon information by a larger and larger set of managers and investors, as well as increased concern with the relationships between goals and objectives of private entities and society, has created new problems.

For students of accounting, changes have occurred so fast that new kinds of problems and proposed methods for dealing with them are not treated in textbooks. In addition, problems and solutions often cross boundaries between what were once considered separate disciplines of study. New standards for judging proposed solutions to problems have been suggested, but in many cases these have not been reflected in the learning aids widely available. In many respects, materials which are available do not reveal the unprecedented opportunities for creative thinking and problem solving which accounting presents.

In many respects, the speed of change has made students of all who work with or process accounting information. Those who manage enterprise and social activities and rely upon reports of status and effectiveness must keep pace with changes. Likewise, those who practice as accountants must be continually alert if they are to take advantage of new developments as they occur.

Books in this series were prepared in hopes that they could assist in the development of the processes and greater effectiveness of accounting. Each has been carefully prepared by an outstanding scholar and seeks to focus on one kind of problem, method, or proposal for accounting. We believe these

books bring together materials not widely available until this time. Our goal
has been to make new material available to students in classrooms as well as
to all others who are concerned with improving the processes of accounting.

William J. Bruns, Jr.
Department of Accounting
Graduate School of Business Administration
University of Washington

PREFACE

It is perhaps easiest to describe this book in terms of the three main ways it differs from many previous "quantitatively oriented" accounting textbooks. First, it is an expository text rather than a collection of readings. This approach has been adopted in order to give the book a sharper focus and to control more directly the tone and level of the material. Second, it treats only one area in the range of quantitative tools useful in accounting—matrix methods. Although the book is thus not a smorgasbord of "mathematical accountancy," this does not mean that it is overly narrow in scope. In fact, the author believes that the selected area has at least as much potential applicability in accounting as such other commonly discussed mathematical techniques as the calculus, programming, or statistics. Third, by focusing upon one quantitative tool, the book can present the required mathematical formulations and the accounting applications in one self-contained unit.

The book should be useful as a supplementary text in several different accounting courses. Chapter 2 is designed to be used in conjunction with the treatment of basic bookkeeping procedures in an Elementary Accounting course. Chapter 3 can be used in conjunction with courses in Cost Accounting or Managerial Accounting. Chapter 4 is designed to supplement material which is usually presented in Intermediate Accounting. Chapter 5 is most readily relatable to courses dealing with Financial Planning and Analysis, but it can also be used to supplement the material on Profit Planning, wherever that subject is treated in the curriculum. Chapter 1, which presents the necessary mathematical prerequisites is, of course, required reading in conjunction with any one or more of the other chapters.

Most of the material requires no more mathematical sophistication than that required to successfully complete a good secondary-school algebra course. Thus the unstarred sections should not present any problems to accounting students willing to spend two or three classes with the introductory chapter. The starred sections present more advanced applications and involve techniques presupposing a level of general mathematical sensitivity usually attained in two or three quarters of college mathematics, including some calculus. It should be emphasized, however, that the book is written for students of accounting—not mathematics—and that it is intended to be fully self-contained with respect to the required mathematical concepts and techniques.

The book is designed to bridge the two disciplines of accounting and mathematics. Although these disciplines have been closely linked at a conceptual level since the time of Pacioli, it has only been in recent years that a similar linking has emerged on the practical level. Many teachers of accounting have quite understandably hesitated to adopt a more quantitative emphasis because of a lack of relevant and teachable materials. It is to those persons that the book is directed. The accounting issues with which it deals are well known and widely discussed in the accounting curriculum. They are not just esoteric examples chosen because they happen to "fit" a given quantitative approach. We hope that their relevance as real accounting issues and the highly manageable nature of the matrix methods with which they are treated will combine to make the book "teachable," which, after all, is the fundamental objective of any textbook, quantitatively oriented or not.

I would like to thank Professors J. Leslie Livingstone of The Ohio State University and Russell Barefield of Purdue University for their very constructive criticism of earlier drafts of the manuscript. The help of Professor William Bruns of the University of Washington, who is editor of this series, was also invaluable in bringing the manuscript to its current form. I am of course responsible for any remaining weaknesses in the book.

I would like to dedicate this book to my three sons, J. B., Douglas, and Michael, in the hope that they may someday find as much joy as I have in academic pursuits.

Soldiers Field, Boston   J.K.S.
February 1972

CONTENTS

Chapter One

AN INTRODUCTION
TO MATRIX ALGEBRA

1. DEFINITIONS AND BASIC NOTATION

This chapter will discuss those aspects of matrix mathematics which will be used in the later chapters of the book. First, we must make clear what we mean by the term "matrix." Very simply, a matrix is an array of numbers. For purposes of this book, we will be concerned only with two-dimensional arrays. In general, however, matrices can have three or even more dimensions. The following are examples of two-dimensional arrays of numbers:

$$\begin{bmatrix} 1 & 2 & 4 \\ 5 & 6 & 10 \\ 11 & 12 & 7 \end{bmatrix}, \quad \begin{bmatrix} 0 & 0 \\ 0 & 0 \\ 0 & 0 \\ 0 & 0 \end{bmatrix}, \quad \begin{bmatrix} 1 & 0 \\ 0 & 1 \end{bmatrix}, \quad \begin{bmatrix} 7 & 5 & 3 & 8 \\ 2 & 9 & 6 & 1 \end{bmatrix}.$$

Each such array is a matrix. Brackets around any array emphasize that it is the numbers taken together that form the matrix. The size of a matrix is determined by the number of rows and columns it contains. The first matrix above, for example, has three rows and three columns. The fourth one has two rows and four columns. We will adopt the usual shorthand convention and say that a matrix which has m rows and n columns is of size $m \times n$. Another way of expressing this idea is to say that the matrix is of dimension $m \times n$. For example, the four matrices shown above are, respectively, of size (or dimension) 3×3, 4×2, 2×2, and 2×4. You will note that the number of rows is given first, followed by the number of columns.

We next need some way to designate individual numbers within a matrix. We denote the matrix as an entity by a capital letter. Then we use the same letter in lower case to denote the individual numbers (sometimes called "elements" or "entries") within the matrix. For example, if we use A to denote a matrix, we use a for the individual entries. In order to refer to specific entries in the matrix we need some way of denoting which a we are talking about. Here again we will adopt the usual convention of using subscripts to describe each entry in terms of its row and column position in the matrix. Consider, for example, the following matrix:

$$A = \begin{bmatrix} 1 & 2 & 5 \\ 4 & 6 & 8 \\ 7 & 8 & 3 \end{bmatrix}.$$

For this matrix, $a_{1,2}$ refers to the entry in the first row, second column position. A complete enumeration of this matrix A is:

$$
\begin{array}{lll}
a_{1,1} = 1 & a_{2,1} = 4 & a_{3,1} = 7 \\
a_{1,2} = 2 & a_{2,2} = 6 & a_{3,2} = 8 \\
a_{1,3} = 5 & a_{2,3} = 8 & a_{3,3} = 3.
\end{array}
$$

Thus, for this example, we have

$$A = \begin{bmatrix} a_{11} & a_{12} & a_{13} \\ a_{21} & a_{22} & a_{23} \\ a_{31} & a_{32} & a_{33} \end{bmatrix} = \begin{bmatrix} 1 & 2 & 5 \\ 4 & 6 & 8 \\ 7 & 8 & 3 \end{bmatrix}.$$

To further simplify notation, we will dispense with commas between the two parts of subscripts. From now on, we will write a_{11} instead of $a_{1,1}$ unless the comma is needed for clarity. For example, a comma would be needed for clarity in distinguishing between $a_{11,2}$ and $a_{1,12}$.

2. MATRIX ARITHMETIC: ADDITION AND SUBTRACTION

We now know what a matrix is, how to describe its size, and how to designate individual matrix entries. Our next step is to discuss how we perform arithmetic on matrices. Since you are used to thinking about performing arithmetic on numbers, it should not be particularly unnerving to begin thinking about performing arithmetic on arrays of numbers. The ideas are the same. The arithmetic "operations" we will be concerned with are addition, subtraction, and multiplication. Just as it is possible to add, subtract, or multiply two or more numbers together, it is also possible to perform the same operations on two or more matrices under certain specified conditions. We will deal with each of these three operations in turn.

Addition of matrices is accomplished by adding the corresponding individual elements in the matrices being added. For example, if

$$A = \begin{bmatrix} 1 & 6 \\ 0 & 4 \end{bmatrix} \quad \text{and} \quad B = \begin{bmatrix} 2 & 3 \\ 5 & 0 \end{bmatrix},$$

the matrix sum $[A + B]$ is formed as follows:

$$\begin{bmatrix} 1 + 2 & 6 + 3 \\ 0 + 5 & 4 + 0 \end{bmatrix}.$$

Thus

$$[A + B] = \begin{bmatrix} 3 & 9 \\ 5 & 4 \end{bmatrix}.$$

It is important to note that the sum of two matrices is still a matrix. The addition operation has not changed the fact that we are dealing with arrays of numbers. Because of the way addition of matrices is defined, we also note that it is only possible to add matrices which are of the same size. For example, it is not possible to add the matrices

$$\begin{bmatrix} 1 & 3 \\ 2 & 5 \\ 4 & 6 \\ 8 & 0 \end{bmatrix} \quad \text{and} \quad \begin{bmatrix} 7 & 9 & 5 & 2 \\ 4 & 6 & 11 & 5 \\ 3 & 0 & 0 & 1 \end{bmatrix}.$$

The first matrix does not have a third and fourth column and the second matrix does not have a fourth row. We say that addition of matrices of unequal size is "undefined." As a final point, you can readily see that it is possible to add together more than two matrices (as long as they are all of equal size) simply by performing the additions by pairs. For example, just as with numbers, we have

$$[A + B + C] = [A + [B + C]] = [[A + B] + C].$$

Matrix subtraction is a direct parallel to matrix addition. Formally, the i,jth entry of the matrix difference $[A - B]$ is given by $(a_{ij} - b_{ij})$. Using the same A and B matrices as in the preceding paragraph, for example, we have:

$$[A - B] = \begin{bmatrix} 1 - 2 & 6 - 3 \\ 0 - 5 & 4 - 0 \end{bmatrix} = \begin{bmatrix} -1 & 3 \\ -5 & 4 \end{bmatrix}.$$

All the other points raised in the preceding paragraph also apply to matrix subtraction. Specifically, subtraction is only defined for matrices of equal size; the result of subtracting one matrix from another is a new matrix which has the same size as the first two; and subtractions involving more than two matrices are performed by pairs.

3. MATRIX MULTIPLICATION

Matrix multiplication differs from the direct, component-by-component procedure of matrix addition and subtraction. There are very good reasons why the matrix product $A \cdot B$ is *not* defined to be the matrix of entries $a_{ij} \cdot b_{ij}$, but these reasons are based on advanced concepts of matrix algebra which are beyond the scope of this book. Hence we shall not explain the reasons for the difference but will go on to define matrix multiplication.

You will remember that addition and subtraction were defined only for matrices of equal size. Similarly, multiplication is defined only for matrices whose sizes conform to a certain pattern. Specifically, if matrix A has n columns, the product $A \cdot B$ is only defined for matrices B which have n rows. Thus if matrix C is of size 3×4, matrix D of size 2×4, and matrix E of size 3×2, the only multiplication possible is that of $E \cdot D$. All other combinations are not "conformable" with respect to multiplication. When two matrices are "conformable" for multiplication, the resulting product matrix has the same number of rows as the first matrix of the product and the same number of columns as the second. Thus if A is $m \times n$ and B is $n \times p$, the product $A \cdot B$ will be of size $m \times p$. For example, consider the following matrix multiplication:

$$\begin{bmatrix} a & b \\ c & d \end{bmatrix} \cdot \begin{bmatrix} e & f & i \\ g & h & j \end{bmatrix} = \begin{bmatrix} (ae + bg) & (af + bh) & (ai + bj) \\ (ce + dg) & (cf + dh) & (ci + dj) \end{bmatrix}.$$

$2 \times 2 \qquad 2 \times 3 \qquad\qquad\qquad 2 \times 3$

Let us now turn to a more formal consideration of the actual calculational techniques of matrix multiplication. The i,jth entry of the product matrix $A \cdot B$ is given by

$$\sum_{k=1}^{n} a_{ik} \cdot b_{kj} = a_{i1}b_{1j} + a_{i2}b_{2j} + \cdots + a_{in}b_{nj}.$$

In words, the i,jth entry of the product matrix $A \cdot B$ is formed by multiplying each element in the ith row of A by the corresponding element in the jth column of B and then summing these products. For example, suppose

$$A = \begin{bmatrix} 1 & 5 \\ 2 & 4 \\ 3 & 6 \end{bmatrix} \quad \text{and} \quad B = \begin{bmatrix} 2 & 7 & 0 \\ 9 & 0 & 1 \end{bmatrix}.$$

Since A is of size 3×2 and B is of size 2×3, the matrix product $A \cdot B$ is defined and is of size 3×3. If we denote by C the product matrix $A \cdot B$, then the calculation of each entry c_{ij} is as follows:

$$c_{11} = \sum_{k=1}^{2} a_{1k} \cdot b_{k1} = a_{11} \cdot b_{11} + a_{12} \cdot b_{21} = 1 \cdot 2 + 5 \cdot 9 = 47,$$

$$c_{12} = \sum_{k=1}^{2} a_{1k} \cdot b_{k2} = a_{11} \cdot b_{12} + a_{12} \cdot b_{22} = 1 \cdot 7 + 5 \cdot 0 = 7,$$

$$c_{13} = \sum_{k=1}^{2} a_{1k} \cdot b_{k3} = a_{11} \cdot b_{13} + a_{12} \cdot b_{23} = 1 \cdot 0 + 5 \cdot 1 = 5,$$

$$c_{21} = \sum_{k=1}^{2} a_{2k} \cdot b_{k1} = a_{21} \cdot b_{11} + a_{22} \cdot b_{21} = 2 \cdot 2 + 4 \cdot 9 = 40,$$

$$c_{22} = \sum_{k=1}^{2} a_{2k} \cdot b_{k2} = a_{21} \cdot b_{12} + a_{22} \cdot b_{22} = 2 \cdot 7 + 4 \cdot 0 = 14,$$

$$c_{23} = \sum_{k=1}^{2} a_{2k} \cdot b_{k3} = a_{21} \cdot b_{13} + a_{22} \cdot b_{23} = 2 \cdot 0 + 4 \cdot 1 = 4,$$

$$c_{31} = \sum_{k=1}^{2} a_{3k} \cdot b_{k1} = a_{31} \cdot b_{11} + a_{32} \cdot b_{21} = 3 \cdot 2 + 6 \cdot 9 = 60,$$

$$c_{32} = \sum_{k=1}^{2} a_{3k} \cdot b_{k2} = a_{31} \cdot b_{12} + a_{32} \cdot b_{22} = 3 \cdot 7 + 6 \cdot 0 = 21,$$

$$c_{33} = \sum_{k=1}^{2} a_{3k} \cdot b_{k3} = a_{31} \cdot b_{13} + a_{32} \cdot b_{23} = 3 \cdot 0 + 6 \cdot 1 = 6.$$

In summary, we have

$$A \cdot B = \begin{bmatrix} 1 & 5 \\ 2 & 4 \\ 3 & 6 \end{bmatrix} \cdot \begin{bmatrix} 2 & 7 & 0 \\ 9 & 0 & 1 \end{bmatrix} = C = \begin{bmatrix} 47 & 7 & 5 \\ 40 & 14 & 4 \\ 60 & 21 & 6 \end{bmatrix}.$$

You will note that because of the way matrix multiplication is defined, $A \cdot B$ is not usually equal to $B \cdot A$. In fact, in the preceding example, $B \cdot A$ does not even have the same dimensions as $A \cdot B$. The matrix $B \cdot A$ is of the size 2×2 because it is the product of a 2×3 matrix multiplied by a 3×2 matrix instead of the other way around. You can check your understanding of the matrix multiplication technique by going through the following calculation of $B \cdot A$. Let $B \cdot A = D$. Then the entries d_{ij} are computed as follows:

$$d_{11} = \sum_{k=1}^{3} b_{1k} \cdot a_{k1} = b_{11} \cdot a_{11} + b_{12} \cdot a_{21} + b_{13} \cdot a_{31}$$
$$= 2 \cdot 1 + 7 \cdot 2 + 0 \cdot 3 = 16,$$

$$d_{12} = \sum_{k=1}^{3} b_{1k} \cdot a_{k2} = b_{11} \cdot a_{12} + b_{12} \cdot a_{22} + b_{13} \cdot a_{32}$$
$$= 2 \cdot 5 + 7 \cdot 4 + 0 \cdot 6 = 38,$$

$$d_{21} = \sum_{k=1}^{3} b_{2k} \cdot a_{k1} = b_{21} \cdot a_{11} + b_{22} \cdot a_{21} + b_{23} \cdot a_{31}$$
$$= 9 \cdot 1 + 0 \cdot 2 + 1 \cdot 3 = 12,$$

$$d_{22} = \sum_{k=1}^{3} b_{2k} \cdot a_{k2} = b_{21} \cdot a_{12} + b_{22} \cdot a_{22} + b_{23} \cdot a_{32}$$
$$= 9 \cdot 5 + 0 \cdot 4 + 1 \cdot 6 = 51.$$

In summary, we have

$$B \cdot A = \begin{bmatrix} 2 & 7 & 0 \\ 9 & 0 & 1 \end{bmatrix} \cdot \begin{bmatrix} 1 & 5 \\ 2 & 4 \\ 3 & 6 \end{bmatrix} = D = \begin{bmatrix} 16 & 38 \\ 12 & 51 \end{bmatrix}.$$

In forming the matrix product $A \cdot B$, we say that we are "pre-multiplying" B by A. Conversely, we could say that we are "post-multiplying" A by B.

4. SCALAR MULTIPLICATION

We also need to mention the multiplication of a matrix times a number. In the context of matrix mathematics, a single number or constant taken by itself is called a "scalar." Multiplication of a constant (scalar) times a matrix is defined just like matrix addition and subtraction and thus does not require lengthy explanation. If b is a scalar and A is a matrix, the product $b \cdot A$ is a matrix each entry of which is given by $b \cdot a_{ij}$. Thus if

$$A = \begin{bmatrix} 2 & 1 \\ 4 & 0 \end{bmatrix},$$

the product $3 \cdot A$ is given by

$$\begin{bmatrix} 3 \cdot 2 & 3 \cdot 1 \\ 3 \cdot 4 & 3 \cdot 0 \end{bmatrix} = \begin{bmatrix} 6 & 3 \\ 12 & 0 \end{bmatrix}.$$

Unlike the situation in which a matrix is multiplied by a matrix, "pre-multiplying" and "post-multiplying" are defined the same way when a matrix is multiplied by a scalar. That is, we define Ab to be the same as bA. In other words, for a matrix A and a scalar b, we have $Ab = bA$.

5. MATRIX INVERSION

We have not talked at all about division because that operation is not defined for matrices. However, you are aware that in dealing with numbers, an alternative procedure to dividing something by x is to multiply it by the reciprocal of x, $\dfrac{1}{x}$. Another name for the reciprocal of x is the inverse, denoted by x^{-1}. That is, $\dfrac{1}{x} = x^{-1}$. In this sense, one can also talk about matrix "division" under certain specified conditions. If a matrix A has the same number of rows as it has columns (a square matrix) and fulfills certain other technical conditions which are usually met in practical accounting applications, one can compute the inverse matrix of A, denoted by A^{-1}. This inverse matrix A^{-1} can be used as a matrix in any of the ways we have already discussed. More formally, for any square matrix A, the inverse matrix A^{-1} (if it exists, and we will always assume that it does) is defined to be the matrix such that $A \cdot A^{-1} = I$. The matrix I in this equation is a special square matrix of the same size as A. It has the number one in each position on the diagonal which runs from upper left to lower right (main diagonal) and has zeros in all other positions. Such a matrix is called an "identity matrix." The 2 × 2 and 3 × 3 identity matrices, for example, look like this:

$$\begin{bmatrix} 1 & 0 \\ 0 & 1 \end{bmatrix}, \qquad \begin{bmatrix} 1 & 0 & 0 \\ 0 & 1 & 0 \\ 0 & 0 & 1 \end{bmatrix}.$$

You will note that the identity matrix serves the same purpose in matrix arithmetic that the number 1 serves in the conventional arithmetic with which you are already familiar. Specifically, in dealing with numbers, we know that $x(1/x) = x \cdot x^{-1} = 1$. The direct parallel in a matrix situation is: $A \cdot A^{-1} = I$.

Because the inverse of a square matrix is a very important quantity which is used over and over again in applications of matrix mathematics, it is important for you to understand how an inverse is computed. As you will soon see, however, the calculations are very tedious and time-consuming, even though the approach is not really complex. In any really significant application, one always makes use of electronic computers in calculating inverses. Because we are only trying to illustrate the technique, we will concentrate here on two very simple examples. Basically, the technique is as follows.

1. Form a new augmented matrix which consists of the matrix to be inverted alongside an identity matrix of the same size.

2. Perform row operations on the entire augmented matrix until the part representing the matrix to be inverted is reduced to an identity matrix.
3. The part originally composed of an identity matrix will now contain the desired inverse.

The "row operations" referred to above are calculational procedures which are performed on individual rows of the augmented matrix. The following are the so-called "elementary" row operations.

1. Multiply each of the components in a row by any number (except zero) or fraction and replace the row by this new revised row.
2. Add any two rows together, component-by-component, and replace either of the two rows by this new sum row.
3. Interchange any two rows.

There are other valid row operations, but these three are the only ones we need to use in performing matrix inversions. These operations can be performed over and over again in any order until the desired result is achieved.

Let us illustrate the technique by calculating the inverse of the matrix

$$A = \begin{bmatrix} 3 & 2 \\ 5 & 4 \end{bmatrix}.$$

1. First form the augmented matrix

$$\left[\begin{array}{cc|cc} 3 & 2 & 1 & 0 \\ 5 & 4 & 0 & 1 \end{array} \right].$$

2. Multiply the second row by $\frac{1}{4}$ in order to bring a 1 into the a_{22} position.

$$\left[\begin{array}{cc|cc} 3 & 2 & 1 & 0 \\ \frac{5}{4} & 1 & 0 & \frac{1}{4} \end{array} \right].$$

3. Multiply the second row by -2 and add it to the first row in order to bring a zero into the a_{12} position:

$$\left[\begin{array}{cc|cc} \frac{1}{2} & 0 & 1 & -\frac{1}{2} \\ \frac{5}{4} & 1 & 0 & \frac{1}{4} \end{array} \right].$$

4. Multiply the first row by $-\frac{5}{2}$ and add it to the second row in order to bring a zero into the a_{21} position:

$$\left[\begin{array}{cc|cc} \frac{1}{2} & 0 & 1 & -\frac{1}{2} \\ 0 & 1 & -\frac{5}{2} & \frac{3}{2} \end{array}\right].$$

5. Multiply the first row by 2 in order to bring a 1 into the a_{11} position:

$$\left[\begin{array}{cc|cc} 1 & 0 & 2 & -1 \\ 0 & 1 & -\frac{5}{2} & \frac{3}{2} \end{array}\right].$$

We are now finished, because the left half of the augmented matrix is an identity matrix. A^{-1} is represented by what remains in the right half of the augmented matrix, namely,

$$A^{-1} = \left[\begin{array}{cc} 2 & -1 \\ -\frac{5}{2} & \frac{3}{2} \end{array}\right].$$

To verify our calculations, we can demonstrate that $A \cdot A^{-1}$ does, in fact, equal the identity matrix. Test your understanding of matrix multiplication by verifying that

$$A \cdot A^{-1} = \left[\begin{array}{cc} 3 & 2 \\ 5 & 4 \end{array}\right] \cdot \left[\begin{array}{cc} 2 & -1 \\ -\frac{5}{2} & \frac{3}{2} \end{array}\right] = \left[\begin{array}{cc} 1 & 0 \\ 0 & 1 \end{array}\right].$$

To establish this technique more firmly in your mind, we will go through a second example. This time we will compute the inverse of

$$B = \left[\begin{array}{ccc} 3 & 2 & 0 \\ 4 & 3 & 1 \\ 0 & 5 & 2 \end{array}\right].$$

1. First form the augmented matrix

$$\left[\begin{array}{ccc|ccc} 3 & 2 & 0 & 1 & 0 & 0 \\ 4 & 3 & 1 & 0 & 1 & 0 \\ 0 & 5 & 2 & 0 & 0 & 1 \end{array}\right].$$

2. Next, multiply the third row by $\frac{1}{2}$ in order to bring a 1 into the b_{33} position:

$$
\left[
\begin{array}{ccc|ccc}
3 & 2 & 0 & 1 & 0 & 0 \\
4 & 3 & 1 & 0 & 1 & 0 \\
0 & \frac{5}{2} & 1 & 0 & 0 & \frac{1}{2}
\end{array}
\right].
$$

3. Multiply row 3 by -1 and add it to row 2 in order to bring a zero into position b_{23}:

$$
\left[
\begin{array}{ccc|ccc}
3 & 2 & 0 & 1 & 0 & 0 \\
4 & \frac{1}{2} & 0 & 0 & 1 & -\frac{1}{2} \\
0 & \frac{5}{2} & 1 & 0 & 0 & \frac{1}{2}
\end{array}
\right].
$$

4. Multiply row 2 by 2 to bring a 1 into position b_{22}:

$$
\left[
\begin{array}{ccc|ccc}
3 & 2 & 0 & 1 & 0 & 0 \\
8 & 1 & 0 & 0 & 2 & -1 \\
0 & \frac{5}{2} & 1 & 0 & 0 & \frac{1}{2}
\end{array}
\right].
$$

5. Multiply row 2 by -2 and add it to row 1 in order to bring a zero into position b_{12}:

$$
\left[
\begin{array}{ccc|ccc}
-13 & 0 & 0 & 1 & -4 & 2 \\
8 & 1 & 0 & 0 & 2 & -1 \\
0 & \frac{5}{2} & 1 & 0 & 0 & \frac{1}{2}
\end{array}
\right].
$$

6. Multiply row 1 by $-\frac{1}{13}$ to bring a 1 into position b_{11}:

$$
\left[
\begin{array}{ccc|ccc}
1 & 0 & 0 & -\frac{1}{13} & \frac{4}{13} & -\frac{2}{13} \\
8 & 1 & 0 & 0 & 2 & -1 \\
0 & \frac{5}{2} & 1 & 0 & 0 & \frac{1}{2}
\end{array}
\right].
$$

7. Multiply row 1 by -8 and add to row 2 in order to bring a zero into

position b_{21}:

$$\begin{bmatrix} 1 & 0 & 0 & \bigm| & -\frac{1}{13} & \frac{4}{13} & -\frac{2}{13} \\ 0 & 1 & 0 & \bigm| & \frac{8}{13} & -\frac{6}{13} & \frac{3}{13} \\ 0 & \frac{5}{2} & 1 & \bigm| & 0 & 0 & \frac{1}{2} \end{bmatrix}.$$

8. Multiply row 2 by $-\frac{5}{2}$ and add to row 3 in order to bring a zero into position b_{32}:

$$\begin{bmatrix} 1 & 0 & 0 & \bigm| & -\frac{1}{13} & \frac{4}{13} & -\frac{2}{13} \\ 0 & 1 & 0 & \bigm| & \frac{8}{13} & -\frac{6}{13} & \frac{3}{13} \\ 0 & 0 & 1 & \bigm| & -\frac{20}{13} & \frac{15}{13} & -\frac{1}{13} \end{bmatrix}.$$

Since the left half of the augmented matrix has now been reduced to an identity matrix, we know that we are finished. You should be able to verify that

$$B^{-1} = \begin{bmatrix} -\frac{1}{13} & \frac{4}{13} & -\frac{2}{13} \\ \frac{8}{13} & -\frac{6}{13} & \frac{3}{13} \\ -\frac{20}{13} & \frac{15}{13} & -\frac{1}{13} \end{bmatrix}.$$

As a hint, remember that $B \cdot B^{-1} = I$.

These two examples should convince you that matrix inversion is a straightforward but also very tedious procedure. It is nevertheless very useful and we will refer to it many times in later chapters.

6. THE ZERO MATRIX

Another special matrix we will be using many times is the zero matrix, which is composed of all zero entries. Unlike the identity matrix, which must be square, a zero matrix can be any size at all. The following are all examples of zero matrices:

$$\begin{bmatrix} 0 & 0 \\ 0 & 0 \end{bmatrix}, \quad \begin{bmatrix} 0 & 0 & 0 \\ 0 & 0 & 0 \end{bmatrix}, \quad \begin{bmatrix} 0 & 0 \\ 0 & 0 \\ 0 & 0 \\ 0 & 0 \end{bmatrix}.$$

Before you conclude that this is a trivial concept, it is worth considering that such matrices are the equivalent of the number 0 in regular arithmetic. Many mathematicians consider the invention of 0 to be the single most important step in the development of the theory underlying modern arithmetic. In this book we will use the capital letter O to represent a zero matrix. The size of O will be determined by the context in which it is presented.

Basically, we will make use of the following three properties of zero matrices.

1. $A + O = A$, for any matrix A.
2. $A - O = A$, for any matrix A.
3. $A \cdot O = O$, for any matrix A.

Each of these properties is really a theorem which we could prove, using formal techniques of mathematical logic. However, since this book is oriented toward accounting applications, we will only state the theorems we want to use and will not take the time to prove them.

7. THE TRANSPOSE OF A MATRIX

Another concept we will be using is the transpose of a matrix A, denoted A^T. The idea of the transpose is to switch the rows and columns so that what was row 1 is now column 1, what was row 2 is now column 2, and so on. Consider, for example, the following three matrices:

$$A = \begin{bmatrix} 1 & 2 & 3 \\ 4 & 5 & 6 \\ 7 & 8 & 9 \end{bmatrix}, \qquad B = \begin{bmatrix} 4 & 3 & 7 & 6 \\ 2 & 1 & 5 & 9 \end{bmatrix}. \qquad C = \begin{bmatrix} 1 & 5 \\ 4 & 9 \\ 6 & 8 \end{bmatrix}.$$

The transpose of each matrix is as follows:

$$A^T = \begin{bmatrix} 1 & 4 & 7 \\ 2 & 5 & 8 \\ 3 & 6 & 9 \end{bmatrix}, \qquad B^T = \begin{bmatrix} 4 & 2 \\ 3 & 1 \\ 7 & 5 \\ 6 & 9 \end{bmatrix}, \qquad C^T = \begin{bmatrix} 1 & 4 & 6 \\ 5 & 9 & 8 \end{bmatrix}.$$

You will note that if A is of size $m \times n$, A^T will be of size $n \times m$. Formally, for any matrix A, A^T is the matrix such that $a_{ij}^T = a_{ji}$.

8. VECTORS

Matrices which have only one row or column recur frequently enough to be given a special name. They are called "vectors." For example the 1×4 matrix $\begin{bmatrix} 1 & 3 & 2 & 5 \end{bmatrix}$ is also called a row vector, since it consists of only one row. Similarly the 5×1 matrix

$$\begin{bmatrix} 2 \\ 3 \\ 7 \\ 9 \\ 1 \end{bmatrix}$$

can be called a column vector, since it consists of only one column.

9. ROW OR COLUMN SUMMATION

Another matrix operation we will be using occasionally in later chapters is row or column summation. This is simply the process of adding together the elements in any one row or column to get a row or column total. We will denote the sum of the elements in the ith row of any matrix A by the symbol $a_{i.}$. Similarly, the jth column sum will be denoted by $a_{.j}$. Formally, for an $m \times n$ matrix A, we define the row and column sums as follows:

$$a_{i.} = \sum_{k=1}^{n} a_{ik}, \qquad i = 1, 2, \ldots, m,$$

$$a_{.j} = \sum_{k=1}^{m} a_{kj}, \qquad j = 1, 2, \ldots, n.$$

We will illustrate these ideas for the 4×3 matrix

$$A = \begin{bmatrix} 1 & 2 & 3 \\ 4 & 3 & 2 \\ 5 & 6 & 7 \\ 8 & 7 & 6 \end{bmatrix}$$

We have

$$a_{1\cdot} = \sum_{k=1}^{3} a_{1k} = a_{11} + a_{12} + a_{13} \qquad = 1 + 2 + 3 = 6,$$

$$a_{2\cdot} = \sum_{k=1}^{3} a_{2k} = a_{21} + a_{22} + a_{23} \qquad = 4 + 3 + 2 = 9,$$

$$a_{3\cdot} = \sum_{k=1}^{3} a_{3k} = \ldots \qquad = 5 + 6 + 7 = 18,$$

$$a_{4\cdot} = \ldots \qquad = 8 + 7 + 6 = 21,$$

$$a_{\cdot 1} = \sum_{k=1}^{4} a_{k1} = a_{11} + a_{21} + a_{31} + a_{41} \quad = 1 + 4 + 5 + 8 = 18,$$

$$a_{\cdot 2} = \sum_{k=1}^{4} a_{k2} = a_{12} + a_{22} + a_{32} + a_{42} \quad = 2 + 3 + 6 + 7 = 18,$$

$$a_{\cdot \beta} = \cdots \qquad = 3 + 2 + 7 + 6 = 18.$$

10. A SUMMARY OF USEFUL PROPERTIES OF MATRICES

We will conclude this chapter with a list of some other properties of matrices which will be used in later chapters. As noted before, each such property is really a theorem which we are offering without proof. Many of them are corollaries of properties already described.

1. $A + B = B + A$.
2. $[A \cdot B \cdot C] = A[BC] = [AB]C$.
3. $[A^{-1}]^{-1} = A$.
4. $[A^{\mathsf{T}}]^{\mathsf{T}} = A$.
5. $[A^{-1}]^{\mathsf{T}} = [A^{\mathsf{T}}]^{-1}$.
6. $[AB]^{\mathsf{T}} = B^{\mathsf{T}}A^{\mathsf{T}}$.
7. $[AB]^{-1} = B^{-1}A^{-1}$ if A and B are both square.
8. $[A - B] \cdot C = AC - BC$.
9. $AI = IA = A$. Note that if A is of dimension $m \times n$, I must be of dimension $n \times n$ for $A \cdot I$ to be defined and of dimension $m \times m$ for $I \cdot A$ to be defined.

10. For any square matrix A, $A^2 = A \cdot A$. In general, $A^n = [A(A)(A) \cdots (A)]$, n times.
11. For any square matrix A, $A^0 = I$. Although there is no common sense to raising something to the zero power, this expression corresponds to the rule in conventional algebra that any number raised to the zero power is equal to one.

SELECTED REFERENCES

1. Almon, Clopper. *Matrix Methods in Economics.* Addison-Wesley, Reading, Mass., 1967. Especially Chapter 1.
2. Corcoran, A. Wayne. *Mathematical Applications in Accounting.* Harcourt, Brace & World, New York, 1968. Especially Chapter 6.
3. Hadley, George. *Linear Algebra.* Addison-Wesley, Reading, Mass., 1961. Especially Chapter 3.
4. Hanes, Bernard. *Mathematics for Management Science.* Charles E. Merrill, Columbus, Ohio, 1962. Especially Chapter 9.
5. Johnston, J. *Econometric Methods.* McGraw-Hill, New York, 1963. Especially Chapter 3.
6. Kemeny, John, Arthur Schleifer, J. Laurie Snell, and Gerald Thompson. *Finite Mathematics with Business Applications.* Prentice-Hall, Englewood Cliffs, N.J., 1962. Especially Chapter 5.
7. Levin, Richard, and C. A. Kirkpatrick. *Quantitative Approaches to Management.* McGraw-Hill, New York, 1965. Especially Chapter 7.
8. Searle, S. R., and W. H. Hausman. *Matrix Algebra for Business and Economics.* Wiley-Interscience, New York, 1970.
9. Springer, Clifford H., Robert E. Herlihy, and Robert I. Boggs. *Basic Mathematics.* Volume 1 of the Mathematics for Management Series, Richard D. Irwin, New York, 1965.

Chapter Two

MATRIX BOOKKEEPING: THE TECHNIQUES OF COMPUTERIZED ACCOUNTING

1. GENERAL LEDGER ACCOUNTING

1.1 INTRODUCTION

We will assume in this chapter that you are already familiar with the fundamentals of transaction analysis and the mechanics of how basic transaction data are summarized and transformed into trial balances and then financial statements. All this comes under the conventional heading of "general-ledger accounting." In this chapter we are interested in applying these ideas to situations in which the general ledger is no longer an actual book entrusted to someone in the accounting department, but rather a set of electronic impulses buried deep in the mass of wires, microcircuits, and flashing lights known as "the computer."

Even if the mode of analysis is now electronic instead of manual or mechanical, the basic task is still the same: to keep systematic track of the financial activities of the company so as to facilitate periodic summarization for the purpose of preparing articulated financial statements. The computer must still be able to handle such concepts as double entry, debits and credits, adjusting entries, and compound transactions. We will examine in the next pages how the computer deals with these items and others like them. The relevance of the subject to this book stems from the fact that, in many computer installations, bookkeeping is done using matrix methods. The application of matrix methods to this traditional part of basic accounting is really the subject of the chapter.

1.2 THE GENERAL LEDGER MATRIX

As a frame of reference for illustrating the techniques of matrix book-keeping, we will use the hypothetical Anderson's Discount Emporium, purveyors of "men's better suits at rock-bottom prices." The chart of accounts for ADE, a sole proprietorship, is a very simple one, as follows:

Account number	Account name
0	Cash
1	Inventory
2	Store fixtures
3	Accumulated depreciation
4	Accounts payable
5	Owner's equity
6	Owner's drawing account
7	Sales
8	Cost of goods sold
9	Other expenses

No real business would actually use this brief a chart of accounts, but we are more concerned for the moment with the clarity of the illustration than with realism. Although ADE is a small business with very simple account-ing needs, the proprietor, Bob Anderson, has decided to hire a computer service bureau to do all the bookkeeping and accounting for the store. The service bureau will use matrix methods in doing the bookkeeping.

The first step in this regard is to construct a blank 10×10 chart-of-accounts matrix in which each column and each row refer to one of the 10 elements in the chart of accounts. As illustrated in Table 2.1, the same information, account names or numbers, is repeated in designating rows and columns. The result is a blank array, stored in the memory of the computer, into which basic transaction data can be entered. This matrix will serve as the equivalent of a general ledger, or L.

1.3 TRANSACTION ANALYSIS

The next step is to specify a procedure for entering transaction data into this rather strange-looking ledger. Since all entries are made up of debits and credits and the matrix is composed of rows and columns, we can adopt a convenient convention that debits correspond to rows and credits to columns. We then no longer need to write things down twice to preserve

Table 2.1.   General-ledger matrix L

	Cash	Inventory	Store fixtures	Accum. depreciation	Accounts payable	Owner's equity	Drawing account	Sales	Cost of goods sold	Other expenses
	0	1	2	3	4	5	6	7	8	9
0 Cash										
1 Inventory										
2 Store fixtures										
3 Accum. depreciation										
4 Accounts payable .										
5 Owner's equity										
6 Drawing account										
7 Sales										
8 Cost of goods sold										
9 Other expenses										

the double entry convention because each element in the ledger matrix already has a double designation: namely, its row location and its column location. Thus if Mr. Anderson sells a suit for $50. in cash, it is not necessary to enter a $50. debit in the cash account and a $50. credit in the sales account. Instead, we need only enter $50. in cell l_{07}, since this cell is the one representing entries which involve a debit to cash (account 0) and a credit to sales (account 7).

Since the ledger matrix does not really exist anywhere other than in the memory of the computer, a more correct statement about how this transaction gets entered is to say that we tell the computer to add $50. to the total which is stored in location l_{07}. Since this is not a book about computer programming, we won't go into much detail about how such an order to the computer would actually be written. In most programming languages, however, the instruction would look something like this:

$$l_{07} = l_{07} + 50.$$

This is a specialized use of the "equal" sign, and it clearly does not mean that the left side equals the right side. What it does represent is a command to the computer to take what appears on the right side of the equal sign and put it in the location indicated on the left side of the sign. This instruction thus tells the computer to put the sum of what is in l_{07} plus 50. into the location l_{07}. The result is clearly the addition of 50. to l_{07}, which is what we wanted.

To strengthen your understanding of this technique for recording transactions, consider the following three additional examples.

1. *Transaction:* Mr. Anderson buys $3000. worth of merchandise on account.
   Traditional ledger Entry: Dr. Inventory (account 1)   3000.
   Cr. Accounts payable (account 4)   3000.
   Ledger matrix entry: $l_{14} = l_{14} + 3000.$
2. *Transaction:* Anderson pays a bill totaling $100 for newspaper advertisements for the current week.
   Traditional ledger entry: Dr. Other expenses (account 9)   100.
   Cr. Cash (account 0)   100.
   Ledger matrix entry: $l_{90} = l_{90} + 100.$
3. *Transaction:* Depreciation expense for the month is $200.
   Traditional ledger entry: Dr. Other expenses (account 9)   200.
   Cr. Accumulated depreciation   200.
   (account 3)
   Ledger matrix entry: $l_{93} = l_{93} + 200.$

1.4 COMPOUND TRANSACTIONS

The above approach works only for "simple" transactions in which one account is debited and one account credited for the same amount. In order to process "compound" transactions in which individual debit and credit amounts do not match, we need to adopt some kind of simplifying convention. For example, consider how we would record the entry if Mr. Anderson purchased $1000. worth of regular merchandise and $100. worth of material samples (to be expensed) from the same vendor on account. In a regular manual or mechanized ledger, the entry would be:

Dr. Inventory (account 1)   1000.
Other expenses (account 9)   100.
Cr. Accounts payable (account 4)   1100.

In the matrix ledger, however, we cannot use the approach outlined earlier because individual debits do not match the credit amount. What we must do is break the entry down into pieces which do contain matched debit and credit amounts. This segmenting process is purely arbitrary and it is not really important how an entry is broken down, as long as the pieces add up to the proper compound entry. In the example at hand, it seems most logical to segment the entry as follows:

$$l_{14} = l_{14} + 1000.$$
$$l_{94} = l_{94} + 100.$$

Many times, however, there is not such an obvious way to break up the entry. Consider, for example, the situation in which a display rack originally costing $100. with a remaining book value of $50. is sold for $65. in cash. The compound entry is:

Dr. Cash (account 0)   65.
    Accumulated depreciation (account 3)   50.
Cr. Store fixtures (account 2)   100.
    Drawing account (account 6)   15.

In this case, there is no clearly logical way to segment the entry. One way which works is the following:

$$l_{02} = l_{02} + 65.$$
$$l_{32} = l_{32} + 35.$$
$$l_{36} = l_{36} + 15.$$

Since the selection is arbitrary, you might choose instead to record the transaction this way:

$$l_{02} = l_{02} + 50.$$
$$l_{06} = l_{06} + 15.$$
$$l_{32} = l_{32} + 50.$$

Either approach results in total debits to cash (account 0) for $65. and to accumulated depreciation (account 3) for $50., and total credits to store fixtures (account 2) for $100. and to the drawing account (account 6) for $15. Thus either approach is acceptable. As long as you are careful to preserve the proper totals in a compound entry, you may segment it into simple entries in any way you choose.

1.5 THE TRIAL BALANCING OPERATION

After the basic transaction data for a period have all been entered in the matrix ledger, the next step is to summarize them in the form of an unadjusted trial balance. For this purpose, we will create a $1 \times n$ balance matrix (or row vector) T, in which n refers to the number of elements in the chart of accounts. For our example, ADE, n equals 10. We will also establish the convention that debits are pluses and credits are minuses, so that when we see items in the trial-balance vector T, we will be able to distinguish debit from credit balances. Since the entries in the ith row of the ledger matrix represent all the debits to account number i and the entries in the ith column represent all the credits to this account, the net impact of transactions during a period on account number i can be computed by subtracting the ith column sum from the ith row sum. The net effect is a debit if the difference is positive, and a credit if it is negative.

Thus we can compile an unadjusted trial balance at any point in time by just updating the prior-period balances by the net impact of current-period transactions. Assuming that the entries t_i initially reflect the prior-period balances in each account, we can accomplish the current-period trial balancing by the following generalized computer instruction.

$$\text{For each account } i, \text{ let } t_i = t_i + \sum_{k=1}^{10} l_{ik} - \sum_{k=1}^{10} l_{ki}.$$

Remembering the column and row summation notation we presented in Chapter 1, we can write the instruction as follows.

$$\text{For } i = 1, 2, \ldots, 10, \text{ let } t_i = t_i + l_{i\bullet} - l_{\bullet i}$$

To verify that T is in balance, we can check the relation $\Sigma_{i=1}^{10} t_i = 0$. Since debits are pluses and credits are minuses and total debits should equal total credits, the sum of all entries in the T vector should be zero. If T was in balance at the beginning of the period, the procedures described above will not disturb the balance condition. In aggregate terms, we have added the sum of each row of L to T and substracted from it the sum of each column of L. The sum of all row totals in L must be the same as the sum of all column totals, because total debits equal total credits. Thus the aggregate value of T must remain zero.

1.6 ADJUSTING AND CLOSING PROCEDURES

Once monthly transaction data have been transferred from the ledger matrix to an updated trial-balance vector, the matrix itself must be cleared so that it is ready to receive the next batch of transaction information. This can be accomplished by the following generalized computer instructions:

$$l_{ij} = 0, \qquad i = 1, 2, \ldots, 10,$$
$$j = 1, 2, \ldots, 10.$$

At this point, all necessary adjusting entries can be posted to the ledger matrix. Once they are posted to the ledger, an adjusted trial balance can be generated by just repeating the trial-balancing operations described in the preceding section. Similarly, one can prepare a post-closing trial balance by zeroing out the ledger matrix again, posting closing entries to it, and then repeating the trial-balancing operation. Once this has been done, the ledger matrix must again be zeroed out so that it is ready to receive basic transaction data for the following period. Let us now review this process from start to finish.

Assume that T initially contains prior-period post-closing balances and L initially is a zero matrix:

1. Post all basic transaction data to the ledger matrix.
2. Prepare an unadjusted trial balance by updating T. Have the computer print out T to provide a tangible record at this stage of the cycle.
3. Zero out the ledger matrix.
4. Post the adjusting entries to the ledger matrix.
5. Prepare an adjusted trial balance by updating T again. Print out T again.
6. Zero out the ledger matrix again.
7. Post the closing entries to the ledger matrix.
8. Prepare a post-closing trial balance by updating T for the third and final time. Print out T again.
9. Zero out the ledger matrix for the third and final time to prepare it for the new cycle to begin the next period.

1.7 AN ILLUSTRATION OF MATRIX BOOKKEEPING

We will illustrate this cycle for the Anderson Discount Emporium by focusing on the details of its financial history during the first month of its existence. That history is as follows.

April 1, 1971   1. Mr. Anderson leased 600 square feet of space in a new shopping center near his home. The rent of $300.

per month was payable each month in advance. He paid one month's rent.

2. He opened a new bank account for the store with a deposit of $25,000.

3. He also purchased $4200. worth of store fixtures, display racks, and decorator items for cash. He estimated that these items would last five years with no salvage value.

4. He also purchased 200 suits for inventory. The suits cost him $48. each. The payment terms were n/30.

5. He hired two part-time sales clerks to help him in the store.

April 2, 1971   6. Anderson's Discount Emporium opened for business.

April 9, 1971   7. Mr. Anderson paid a bill for $500. for advertising in the local newspaper during his first week of business.

April 16, 1971   8. Mr. Anderson paid wages of $500. for the first two weeks.

April 24, 1971   9. Mr. Anderson received a bill of $50. for heat and light through April 21. He planned to pay it early in May.

10. He received a bill of $75. for telephone services through April 22. He paid it in cash.

April 26, 1971   11. Mr. Anderson bought an additional 100 suits at $48. each. The same payment terms applied.

April 27, 1971   12. Mr. Anderson paid $9600. on account to his supplier of suits.

April 28, 1971   13. Mr. Anderson paid $300. to the local radio station for advertising announcements during April.

April 30, 1971   14. Mr. Anderson paid wages of $500. for the last two weeks of April.

15. He noted that he had sold 105 suits during the month at $80. each. All the sales were for cash.

16. He estimated that he owed the following amounts

for April which had not yet been billed to him:
Heat and power $50.
Telephone   25.
Advertising   200.
Supplies   100.

17. He estimated that he owed $200. in payroll taxes for the month of April.

18. He calculated depreciation expense for the month to be $70.

With this information, we can summarize the basic transaction data for the month as follows. The reference numbers refer to the numbers in the chronological history for the month.

1. $l_{90} = l_{90} + 300.$
2. $l_{05} = l_{05} + 25000.$
3. $l_{20} = l_{20} + 4200.$
4. $l_{14} = l_{14} + 9600.$
5.   No entry
6.   No entry
7. $l_{90} = l_{90} + 500.$
8. $l_{90} = l_{90} + 500.$
9. $l_{94} - l_{94} + 50.$
10. $l_{90} = l_{90} + 75.$
11. $l_{14} = l_{14} + 4800.$
12. $l_{40} = l_{40} + 9600.$
13. $l_{90} = l_{90} + 300.$
14. $l_{90} = l_{90} + 500.$
15. $l_{07} = l_{07} + 8400.$
      $l_{81} = l_{81} + 5040.$

At this point, the ledger matrix would appear as in Table 2.2.

With this information, we can construct the unadjusted trial balance as follows:

$$t_0 = t_0 + l_{0.} - l_{.0} = 0 + (25000 + 8400) - (4200 + 9600 + 2175)$$
$$= 17425,$$
$$t_1 = t_1 + l_{.1} - l_{.1} = 0 + 14400 - 5040 \qquad = 9360,$$
$$t_2 = \cdots = 0 + 4200 - 0 \qquad\qquad\qquad = 4200,$$
$$t_3 = \cdots = 0 + 0 - 0 \qquad\qquad\qquad\qquad = 0,$$

Table 2.2.

	0	1	2	3	4	5	6	7	8	9
0	0	0	0	0	0	25,000	0	8400	0	0
1	0	0	0	0	14,400	0	0	0	0	0
2	4200	0	0	0	0	0	0	0	0	0
3	0	0	0	0	0	0	0	0	0	0
4	9600	0	0	0	0	0	0	0	0	0
5	0	0	0	0	0	0	0	0	0	0
6	0	0	0	0	0	0	0	0	0	0
7	0	0	0	0	0	0	0	0	0	0
8	0	5040	0	0	0	0	0	0	0	0
9	2175	0	0	0	50	0	0	0	0	0

$$
\begin{aligned}
t_4 &= \cdots = 0 + 9600 - 14450 & &= -4850, \\
t_5 &= \cdots = 0 + 0 - 25000 & &= -25000, \\
t_6 &= \cdots = 0 + 0 - 0 & &= 0, \\
t_7 &= \cdots = 0 + 0 - 8400 & &= -8400, \\
t_8 &= \cdots = 0 + 5040 - 0 & &= 5040, \\
t_9 &= \cdots = 0 + (2175 + 50) - 0 & &= 2225.
\end{aligned}
$$

We can verify that the trial balance is in balance by computing the sum of the elements in the vector T. Specifically,

$$
\sum_{i=0}^{9} t_i = 17425 + 9360 + 4200 + 0 - 4850 - 25000 - 0 - 8400 + 5040 + 2225 = 0.
$$

After zeroing out the ledger matrix, the next step in the bookkeeping cycle is to enter the adjusting entries. Returning to the chronological history for the reference numbers and using matrix notation, we have the following adjusting entries:

16. $l_{94} = l_{94} + 375.$
17. $l_{94} = l_{94} + 200.$
18. $l_{93} = l_{93} + 70.$

After posting to the ledger matrix, the only row in the matrix which would have any nonzero elements would be row 9. It would appear as follows:

0   0   0   70   575   0   0   0   0   0

The next step is to prepare an adjusted trial balance by updating the vector T for the new data in the ledger matrix. Specifically, we have

$$
\begin{aligned}
t_0 &= t_0 + l_{0.} - l_{.0} = 17425 + 0 - 0 = 17425, \\
t_1 &= t_1 + l_{1.} - l_{.1} = 9360 + 0 - 0 = 9360, \\
t_2 &= \cdots \qquad\qquad = 4200 + 0 - 0 = 4200, \\
t_3 &= \cdots \qquad\qquad = 0 + 0 - 70 = -70, \\
t_4 &= \cdots \qquad\qquad = -4850 + 0 - 575 = -5425, \\
t_5 &= \cdots \qquad\qquad = 250000 + 0 - 0 = 25000, \\
t_6 &= \cdots \qquad\qquad = 0 + 0 - 0 = 0, \\
t_7 &= \cdots \qquad\qquad = -8400 + 0 - 0 = -8400, \\
t_8 &= \cdots \qquad\qquad = 5040 + 0 - 0 = 5040, \\
t_9 &= \cdots \qquad\qquad = 2225 + 645 - 0 = 2870.
\end{aligned}
$$

You can verify for yourself that the adjusted trial balance is in balance. Remember that the sum of the elements must equal zero.

Although businesses do not usually close the books each month, we will close the books for ADE at the end of April to illustrate this final aspect of the matrix bookkeeping cycle. The adjusted trial balance is as follows:

$$
T = \begin{bmatrix} 17425 & 9360 & 4200 & -70 & -5425 & -25000 & 0 & -8400 & 5040 & 2870 \end{bmatrix}.
$$

To close the books, we need only zero out accounts 7, 8, and 9 and transfer the net balance from them to account 6. This can be accomplished by first zeroing out the ledger matrix, next posting the following entries to L, and then updating T by the new balances in L. The necessary entries are

$$
\begin{aligned}
l_{76} &= l_{76} + 8400, \\
l_{68} &= l_{68} + 5040, \\
l_{69} &= l_{69} + 2870.
\end{aligned}
$$

After these entries are posted to L, the ledger matrix would appear as in Table 2.3.

Updating T for the third and final time, we have

$$
\begin{aligned}
t_0 &= t_0 + l_{0.} - l_{.0} = 17425 + 0 - 0 & = 17425, \\
t_1 &= \cdots & = 9360, \\
t_2 &= \cdots & = 4200,
\end{aligned}
$$

Table 2.3.

	0	1	2	3	4	5	6	7	8	9
0	0	0	0	0	0	0	0	0	0	0
1	0	0	0	0	0	0	0	0	0	0
2	0	0	0	0	0	0	0	0	0	0
3	0	0	0	0	0	0	0	0	0	0
4	0	0	0	0	0	0	0	0	0	0
5	0	0	0	0	0	0	0	0	0	0
6	0	0	0	0	0	0	0	0	5040	2870
7	0	0	0	0	0	0	8400	0	0	0
8	0	0	0	0	0	0	0	0	0	0
9	0	0	0	0	0	0	0	0	0	0

$$
\begin{aligned}
t_3 &= \cdots & &= -70, \\
t_4 &= \cdots & &= -5425, \\
t_5 &= \cdots & &= -25000, \\
t_6 &= t_6 + l_{6\cdot} - l_{\cdot 6} = 0 + 7910 - 8400 & &= -490, \\
t_7 &= t_7 + l_{7\cdot} - l_{\cdot 7} = -8400 + 8400 - 0 & &= 0, \\
t_8 &= t_8 + l_{8\cdot} - l_{\cdot 8} = 5040 + 0 - 5040 & &= 0, \\
t_9 &= t_9 + l_{9\cdot} - l_{\cdot 9} = 2820 + 0 - 2820 & &= 0.
\end{aligned}
$$

Thus, the post-closing trial balance is given by

$$T = \begin{bmatrix} 17425 & 9360 & 4200 & -70 & -5375 & -25000 & -490 & 0 & 0 & 0 \end{bmatrix}.$$

After zeroing out the ledger matrix, we would be ready to begin the cycle again for the month of May.

Taken from the adjusted trial balance, an earnings statement for the month is as follows.

Sales	$8400
Cost of goods sold	5040
Gross margin	3360
Other expenses	2870
Net earnings	$ 490

Taken from the post-closing trial balance, a balance sheet as of April 30, 1971, is as follows.

Assets			Liabilities and owner's equity	
Cash		$17425	Accounts payable	$ 5425
Inventory		9360	Mr. Anderson: Capital	25000
Store fixtures	$4200		Drawing	490
Less accumulated				
depreciation	70			
		4130		
		$30915		$30915

We will conclude this chapter by considering an extension of the matrix technique to cover funds-flow accounting.

*2. FUNDS-FLOW ACCOUNTING WITH THE MATRIX LEDGER

2.1 INTRODUCTION

Funds-flow statements have become more and more common in published financial reports in recent years. In Opinion Number 19, the Accounting Principles Board of the American Institute of Certified Public Accountants made the inclusion of such a statement in annual reports mandatory and extended the auditor's opinion to include it.

For many companies, however, a funds-flow statement cannot be prepared directly from the books of account. Its preparation involves special analyses based on changes between two successive balance sheets. Some authors even go so far as to state that the funds statement is necessarily a supplementary or "derived" statement, the information for which comes from the balance sheet and earnings statement, which are more "basic." This is true when the books of account are set up to capture only data for the balance sheet and earnings statement, but the books need not be restricted in this way. Some people believe that funds flows are really the basic transaction data of a firm, and that balance sheets and earnings statements represent the interpreted or "derived" information.

Whichever set of information you consider to be "more basic," one thing is clear. A properly structured set of general accounting procedures

---

*This section can be skipped without loss of continuity.

can capture the necessary information for all three statements at the time of original entry. No special analyses are then required to prepare any of the statements. They all come directly from the books of account. This section of the chapter will illustrate one way to build funds flow accounting into the general ledger, using the matrix approach already outlined. We will adopt the working-capital definition of funds.

2.2 FUNDS-FLOW TRANSACTION ANALYSIS

Just like the duality principle in general accounting which requires that assets equal equities, there is a requirement in funds flow accounting that sources equal uses. Also as in general accounting, this requirement can be interpreted to mean that each transaction must be bookkept in at least two places so as to preserve the equality of assets and equities. The funds-flow double-entry system requires that every transaction be recorded both as a source and as a use of funds. If inventory is sold for cash, for example, there is an increase in working capital by the amount of the sale (a use of funds) and an offsetting increase in funds provided by operations (a source of funds). Similarly, this same transaction involves a decrease in working capital by the amount of the inventory given up (a source of funds) and an offsetting increase in funds used by operations (a use of funds).

This double-entry effect of each transaction on the funds-flow equilibrium of the firm suggests that each transaction can be entered in a funds-flow matrix, identical in purpose to the general-ledger matrix, at the same time it is entered in the ledger matrix. Rather than use a separate funds-flow matrix, it would even be possible to combine the funds-flow and general-ledger matrices into one having four dimensions (a four-dimensional array). In this way, the original entry of a transaction into the matrix L (see Table 2.1) would allow for both funds-flow and general-ledger accounting uses. Such a refinement is beyond the scope of this book, however. Here, we shall consider funds flow as a separate two-dimensional problem.

Transactions of our sample firm can affect the following funds-flow categories.

1. Operations
2. Investment in working capital
3. Long-term debt
4. Owner's equity
5. Investment in store fixtures.

Table 2.4.   Funds-flow matrix F

	Operations	Investment in working capital	Long-term debt	Owner's equity	Investment in store fixtures
	1	2	3	4	5
1. Operations					
2. Investment in working capital					
3. Long-term debt					
4. Owner's equity					
5. Investment in store fixtures					

If we set up a 5×5 funds-flow matrix F (Table 2.4), using these categories as the row and column designators, then every transaction can be entered in it in the same way it is entered in the ledger matrix L. We will adopt the convention that rows represent sources and columns represent uses.

2.3 THE TECHNIQUE ILLUSTRATED

To illustrate the procedure, let us bookkeep the same three sample entries that we considered earlier in this chapter at the end of Section 1.3.

1. *Transaction*: Mr. Anderson buys $3000. worth of merchandise on account.
   Fund matrix entry: $f_{22} = f_{22} + 3000$.

Notice that since this transaction is entered in row 2 and column 2 it will net out to zero when we later compute the overall impact on working capital of all fund transactions for the period; we do this by taking the row sum minus the column sum. This result should seem reasonable when you remember that buying merchandise on account has no impact on the net working capital anyway.

2. *Transaction*: Mr. Anderson pays a bill totaling $100. for newspaper advertisements for the current week.
   Fund matrix entry: $f_{21} = f_{21} + 100$.

This transaction involves a reduction in working capital (a source of funds) and an offsetting reduction in funds provided by operations (a use of funds).

3. *Transaction*:   Depreciation expense for the month is $200.
   Fund matrix entry: No entry!

Remember that depreciation does not involve a flow of funds. The funds-flow event is the purchase or sale of fixed assets. Depreciation simply records the systematic amortization of purchase cost (less estimated salvage value) over the useful life of the asset.

Compound entries can be treated in the same manner as they are in the ledger matrix. Any arbitrary segmentation of the entry is acceptable as long as overall source and use totals are preserved. The previous illustration, involving the disposal of fixed assets at a gain, however, is no longer a good example for this, because it can be handled much more simply in the fund matrix.

Transaction:	Dr. Cash	65.	
	Accumulated depreciation	50.	
	Cr. Store fixtures		100.
	Drawing account		15.

Fund-matrix entry: $f_{52} = f_{52} + 65$.

Accumulated depreciation and gain or loss on disposal are irrelevant in fund accounting. In a funds-flow context, all that has happened is that working capital has been increased by $65. (a use of funds) as a result of the sale of fixed assets (a source of funds).

2.4 GENERATING FUNDS-FLOW STATEMENTS

Once the transactions have been entered, all that remains is to transfer the information in the matrix to a summary 5-component row vector S, which is the basis for preparing a funds-flow statement. The procedure is a direct parallel of the trial-balancing operation explained earlier. Specifically, for each vector element s_i we have

$$s_i = \sum_{k=1}^{5} f_{ik} - \sum_{k=1}^{5} f_{ki} = f_{i\cdot} - f_{\cdot i} .$$

If the sum is positive, the category represents a net source of funds. If the sum is negative, it represents a net use. The funds-flow statement can then be prepared directly from S. The entries s_i should all be zeroed out before proceeding to the next month's transactions so that the vector is again ready to receive the summary data at month's-end.

2.5 FUNDS-FLOW ACCOUNTING FOR ANDERSON'S DISCOUNT EMPORIUM

To more firmly establish your understanding of these ideas and procedures, we will set up each of the transactions in Section 1.7 of this chapter in funds-matrix form and then summarize the results in a vector S, as of month's-end. The reference numbers again refer to the items in the chronological history for April. In matrix notation, the entries are as follows.

1. $f_{21} = f_{21} + 300.$
2. $f_{42} = f_{42} + 25000.$
3. $f_{25} = f_{25} + 4200.$
4. $f_{22} = f_{22} + 9600.$
5. No entry
6. No entry
7. $f_{21} = f_{21} + 500.$
8. $f_{21} = f_{21} + 500.$
9. $f_{21} = f_{21} + 50.$
10. $f_{21} = f_{21} + 75.$
11. $f_{22} = f_{22} + 4800.$
12. $f_{22} = f_{22} + 9600.$
13. $f_{21} = f_{21} + 300.$
14. $f_{21} = f_{21} + 500.$
15. $f_{12} = f_{12} + 8400.$
     $f_{21} = f_{21} + 5040.$
16. $f_{21} = f_{21} + 375.$
17. $f_{21} = f_{21} + 200.$
18. No entry

After these entries are posted to the funds-flow matrix F, the matrix would appear as in Table 2.5.

Table 2.5

	1	2	3	4	5
1	0	8400	0	0	0
2	7840	24000	0	0	4200
3	0	0	0	0	0
4	0	25000	0	0	0
5	0	0	0	0	0

The vector S can be computed in the following way:

$$s_1 = s_1 + f_{1\bullet} - f_{\bullet 1} = 0 + 8400 - 7840 = 560,$$
$$s_2 = s_2 + f_{2\bullet} - f_{\bullet 2} = 0 + (7840 + 24000 + 4200) -$$
$$- (8400 + 24000 + 25000) = -21360,$$
$$s_3 = \cdots \qquad\qquad = 0 + 0 - 0 = 0,$$
$$s_4 = \cdots \qquad\qquad = 0 + 25000 - 0 = 25000,$$
$$s_5 = \cdots \qquad\qquad = 0 + 0 - 4200 = -4200.$$

Thus we have $S = \begin{bmatrix} 560 & -21360 & 0 & 25000 & -4200 \end{bmatrix}$.

We can convert this to the following funds flow statement for April 1971.

Sources of funds		Uses of funds	
Owner's equity	$25000	Investment in store fixtures	$ 4200
Operations	560	Investment in working capital	21360
	$25560		$25560

SELECTED REFERENCES

1. Doney, Lloyd. "Integrating Accounting and Computerized Data Processing," *The Accounting Review*, April 1969.
2. Nolan, Richard. *Fortran IV Computing and Applications.* Addison-Wesley, Reading, Mass. 1971.
3. Tracy, John. *Understanding Accounting.* Prentice-Hall, New York, 1971. Especially Chapter 3.

Chapter Three

MATRIX APPLICATIONS
IN COST ACCOUNTING

1. INTRODUCTION

In this chapter we will present a matrix approach to dealing with three problems in cost accounting. The first concerns the allocation of service-department costs to operating departments for use in developing fully absorbed product costs. The second concerns prime-cost variance computations. The third concerns cost-behavior analysis.

2. OVERHEAD ALLOCATION: SERVICE DEPARTMENTS TO OPERATING DEPARTMENTS

2.1 THE PROBLEM

Consider a hypothetical company which has a departmental organization structure and workflow interrelationships in the manufacturing area as shown in Fig. 3.1.

We will define a four-component column vector E, the elements of which, e_i, represent the total direct costs incurred in the operating departments. Similarly, let F be a three-component column vector representing the total direct costs incurred in the service departments. The problem is to come up with a vector G which represents total costs, both direct and allocated, assigned to each of the operating departments. The difficulty stems from the fact that some service department costs must first be allocated among other service departments before the allocation to operating departments can be made. Since X serves Y, for example, we can't

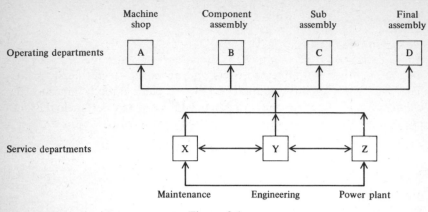

Figure 3.1

allocate Y until X has been allocated. But the fact that Y also serves X means that X can't be allocated until Y is.

2.2 A CALCULATIONAL APPROACH

As an intermediate calculational step, therefore, we also need to define a vector S whose three components represent the total costs for each service department after interdepartmental transfers. As the next calculational step, we need to construct a 7×3 matrix M, whose columns represent the percentages of each service department's costs which are allocated to operating departments and to other service departments. Since all the costs of a service department must be allocated somewhere, each column of M must sum to 100 percent. For calculational convenience, we will break M down into two parts, N and P. In this notation, N is the 4×3 matrix representing allocation percentages to operating departments from service departments, and P is the 3×3 matrix of allocation percentages among service departments. Symbolically, we have

$$M_{7 \times 3} = \left[\frac{N_{4 \times 3}}{P_{3 \times 3}} \right].$$

The horizontal bar does not mean we have formed a fraction, N/P. It just denotes a vertical partitioning of M into two parts. This is similar to the horizontal partitioning we did in Chapter 1 in forming an augmented matrix. Using the above notation, we can write an equation for the vector G, which is what we want to find. Specifically,

$$G = E + N \cdot S. \tag{1}$$

This simply states that G equals the direct costs E of the operating departments, plus the total allocated costs $N \cdot S$ from the service departments. The problem with this equation is that we can't directly measure the elements of S because they are the result of a separate calculational procedure. We can, however, write the following equation for S:

$$S = F + P^{\mathrm{T}} \cdot S. \tag{2}$$

This just states that S equals the direct service department costs F, plus the interdepartmental transfers $P^{\mathrm{T}} \cdot S$.

This is the point at which matrix methods can help us. We can modify the equation so that it involves only elements which are directly measurable. In this way, we can specify a procedure for computing S which in turn allows us to compute G. First, we must rearrange Eq. (2) as follows:

$$S - P^{\mathrm{T}} \cdot S = F. \tag{3}$$

Factoring out S and using properties 8 and 9 from Chapter 1, we can write

$$[I - P^{\mathrm{T}}] \cdot S = F. \tag{4}$$

If we pre-multiply both sides of equation (4) by the matrix quantity $[I - P^{\mathrm{T}}]^{-1}$, we have the following:

$$[I - P^{\mathrm{T}}]^{-1} \cdot [I - P^{\mathrm{T}}] \cdot S = [I - P^{\mathrm{T}}]^{-1} \cdot F,$$

$$I \cdot S = [I - P^{\mathrm{T}}]^{-1} \cdot F,$$

$$S = [I - P^{\mathrm{T}}]^{-1} \cdot F. \tag{5}$$

You will remember from Chapter 1 that any square matrix such as $[I - P^{\mathrm{T}}]$, when multiplied by its inverse $[I - P^{\mathrm{T}}]^{-1}$, equals an identity matrix. This equation for S is now entirely in terms of things we know. It can thus be used to compute S.

Instead of doing this directly however, we will instead substitute equation (5) into equation (1) to obtain

$$G = N \cdot [(I - P^{\mathrm{T}})^{-1} \cdot F] + E. \tag{6}$$

The problem is now reduced to manageable form. We can directly measure N, F, and E, and we can compute the matrix product $[I - P^{\mathrm{T}}]^{-1}$ because P is also known.

2.3 THE TECHNIQUE ILLUSTRATED

In order to illustrate this procedure we will use the following hypothetical data.

$$E = \text{direct costs of operating departments} = \begin{bmatrix} e_1 \\ e_2 \\ e_3 \\ e_4 \end{bmatrix} = \begin{bmatrix} 7100 \\ 6500 \\ 9400 \\ 8700 \end{bmatrix}$$

$$F = \text{direct cost of service departments} = \begin{bmatrix} f_1 \\ f_2 \\ f_3 \end{bmatrix} = \begin{bmatrix} 5600 \\ 7700 \\ 4900 \end{bmatrix}.$$

		From		
		X	Y	Z
To	A	.3	.5	.25
	B	.25	.15	.15
	C	.15	.05	.15
	D	.1	0	.15
	X	0	.1	.15
	Y	.1	0	.15
	Z	.1	.2	0

$$M = \text{allocation-percentages matrix} = \begin{bmatrix} \dfrac{N}{P} \end{bmatrix} =$$

The first step in computing G is to form the matrix $[I - P^{\mathrm{T}}]$:

$$[I - P^{\mathrm{T}}] = \begin{bmatrix} 1 & 0 & 0 \\ 0 & 1 & 0 \\ 0 & 0 & 1 \end{bmatrix} - \begin{bmatrix} 0 & .1 & .1 \\ .1 & 0 & .2 \\ .15 & .15 & 0 \end{bmatrix} = \begin{bmatrix} 1 & -.1 & -.1 \\ -.1 & 1 & -.2 \\ -.15 & -.15 & 1 \end{bmatrix}.$$

The next step is to use row operations to find the inverse of $[I - P^{\mathrm{T}}]$. You can check your understanding of the matrix inversion process by verifying that

$$[I - P^T]^{-1} = \begin{bmatrix} 1.03 & .122 & .128 \\ .137 & 1.046 & .223 \\ .175 & .175 & 1.052 \end{bmatrix}.$$

Next, we form the matrix product $N \cdot [I - P^T]^{-1}$:

$$N[I - P^T]^{-1} = \begin{bmatrix} .3 & .5 & .25 \\ .25 & .15 & .15 \\ .15 & .05 & .15 \\ .1 & 0 & .15 \end{bmatrix} \cdot \begin{bmatrix} 1.03 & .122 & .128 \\ .137 & 1.046 & .223 \\ .175 & .175 & 1.052 \end{bmatrix}$$

$$= \begin{bmatrix} .416 & .601 & .394 \\ .301 & .231 & .205 \\ .172 & .113 & .247 \\ .111 & .055 & .154 \end{bmatrix}.$$

You should note that although we originally made use of the vector S as a calculational step, in actual practice it is not used. Rather than performing the multiplication $[I - P^T]^{-1} \cdot F$ in equation (6), we perform the multiplication $N \cdot [I - P^T]^{-1}$. Unlike the quantity S, which would change each period, the quantity $N \cdot [I - P^T]^{-1}$ will not change as cost levels do. It only changes when we decide to alter the allocation percentages, which is probably only once a year. Thus after we have computed $N \cdot [I - P^T]^{-1}$ once, we normally won't have to compute it again until a year later. Each month we just post-multiply it by F and then add E as follows:

$$G = [(N(I - P^T)]^{-1} \cdot F] + E$$

$$= \begin{bmatrix} .416 & .601 & .394 \\ .301 & .231 & .205 \\ .172 & .113 & .247 \\ .111 & .055 & .154 \end{bmatrix} \cdot \begin{bmatrix} 5600 \\ 7700 \\ 4900 \end{bmatrix} + \begin{bmatrix} 7100 \\ 6500 \\ 9400 \\ 8700 \end{bmatrix}$$

$$G = \begin{bmatrix} 8950 \\ 4450 \\ 3030 \\ 1770 \end{bmatrix} + \begin{bmatrix} 7100 \\ 6500 \\ 9400 \\ 8700 \end{bmatrix} = \begin{bmatrix} 16050 \\ 10950 \\ 12430 \\ 10470 \end{bmatrix}.$$

This technique can be extended to allocate costs to cost-collection centers of any type. A more complicated problem, for example, might involve allocating costs of four operating departments and three service departments to two product cost centers for which the overall flows are represented as in Fig. 3.2.

Although we won't illustrate an example like this here, you can find such an extension of the matrix allocation technique explained in references (3), (11), and (13) at the end of the chapter.

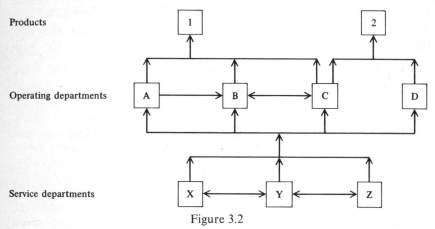

Figure 3.2

3. PRIME-COST VARIANCE COMPUTATIONS

3.1 THE PROBLEM

From your study of variance analysis you know that the formulas for price and quantity variance of material and labor are as follows:

$$PV = AQ(AP - SP),$$
$$QV = SP(AC - SQ),$$
$$TV = AQAP - SCSP = PV + QV,$$

where

$$PV = \text{Price Variance,}$$
$$QV = \text{Quantity Variance,}$$
$$TV = \text{Total Variance,}$$
$$AQ = \text{Actual Quantity used,}$$
$$SQ = \text{Standard Quantity allowed,}$$
$$AP = \text{Actual Price per unit paid,}$$
$$SP = \text{Standard Price per unit allowed.}$$

In this section of the chapter, we will demonstrate that these variances can be expressed in a matrix form which facilitates their calculation in large-scale problems and also provides a convenient format for computerizing the calculations.

We will also illustrate the matrix approach for a hypothetical product Z, the manufacture of which involves two material components and three labor components. We will assume that the company which manufactures Z computes material-price variances at the time of usage and that it is interested in the following information each week:

1. Total price variance for each component
2. Total quantity variance for each component
3. Total material price variance
4. Total labor price variance (labor rate variance)
5. Total material quantity variance (material usage variance)
6. Total labor quantity variance (labor efficiency variance)
7. Total variance for each component
8. A grand total variance.

We will denote by b the number of units of Z produced during the week. Further, we will assume that the company's standard cost records show standard component prices and quantities, SP and SQ, per unit of finished product and that actual quantities AQ used of each component are accumulated in weekly aggregates.

3.2 CALCULATING THE VARIANCES

Since there are five components in the production process, we can think of the price variances for the components as a five-element row vector PV, with entries pv_i.

Similarly, quantity variances and total variances can also be conceived as five-element row vectors QV and TV, with entries qv_i and tv_i.

Actual and standard prices can be thought of as 5×5 matrices AP and SP, which have the prices of the components as their respective main diagonal elements ap_{ii} or sp_{ii}, and zeros elsewhere. Finally, actual and standard quantities can be thought of as five-element row vectors AQ and SQ, with entries aq_i and sq_i. Standard quantities are expressed per unit of finished product whereas we want aggregate variance measures; therefore it is necessary to work with the vector bSQ instead of SQ itself.

Using this notation and expanding the multiplication in the price-variance formula shown in the preceding section, we have for each component

$$pv_i = aq_i \cdot ap_{ii} - aq_i \cdot sp_{ii}.$$

In other words, the vector of price variances is nothing more than the difference between the product of the AQ vector times the AP matrix and the product of the AQ vector times the SP matrix. Similarly, for each component of QV we have

$$qv_i = aq_i \cdot sp_{ii} - b(sq_i) \cdot sp_{ii}.$$

The vector of quantity variances is simply the difference between the product of the AQ vector times the SP matrix and the product of the bSQ vector times the SP matrix. You will note that b is a scalar quantity and thus doesn't complicate the calculation very much at all. If the number of "equivalent units" of production for the labor and material components were not all the same, we could substitute a vector B for the scalar b at this point without adding any real complications. Such a refinement, however, is beyond the scope of this book.

Breaking down the price and quantity variance into total material and labor segments is simply a matter of summing the first two elements and then the last three elements for PV and QV, respectively. Specifically,

$$\text{total material price variance} \quad = \sum_{k=1}^{2} pv_k,$$

$$\text{total labor rate variance} \quad = \sum_{k=3}^{5} pv_k,$$

$$\text{total material usage variance} \quad = \sum_{k=1}^{2} qv_k,$$

$$\text{total labor efficiency variance} = \sum_{k=3}^{5} qv_k.$$

Computing total variances is accomplished by summing all the individual variance elements. Remembering the row summation notation from Chapter 1, we have

$$tv_i = pv_i + qv_i,$$
$$tv_. = pv_. + qv_..$$

This completes the calculations required by management each week. How the variances, once calculated, would be used by management is also beyond the scope of this book.

3.3 AN ILLUSTRATION

Let us now review these variance computations by means of a numerical example. The following information is all known to us:

$$SQ = [5, 3, 2, .5, 4],$$
$$b = 1000,$$
$$AQ = [4950, 3100, 2050, 500, 4600],$$

$$AP = \begin{bmatrix} 1 & 0 & 0 & 0 & 0 \\ 0 & 1.5 & 0 & 0 & 0 \\ 0 & 0 & 2. & 0 & 0 \\ 0 & 0 & 0 & .5 & 0 \\ 0 & 0 & 0 & 0 & 1 \end{bmatrix},$$

$$SP = \begin{bmatrix} 1. & 0 & 0 & 0 & 0 \\ 0 & 2. & 0 & 0 & 0 \\ 0 & 0 & 2. & 0 & 0 \\ 0 & 0 & 0 & .75 & 0 \\ 0 & 0 & 0 & 0 & .5 \end{bmatrix}.$$

We are required to compute all the variances specified in Section 3.1. For calculational convenience in computing price variances, we will form the difference matrix $[AP - SP]$ as follows:

$$[AP - SP] = \begin{bmatrix} 1. & 0 & 0 & 0 & 0 \\ 0 & 1.5 & 0 & 0 & 0 \\ 0 & 0 & 2. & 0 & 0 \\ 0 & 0 & 0 & .5 & 0 \\ 0 & 0 & 0 & 0 & 1. \end{bmatrix} - \begin{bmatrix} 1 & 0 & 0 & 0 & 0 \\ 0 & 2. & 0 & 0 & 0 \\ 0 & 0 & 2. & 0 & 0 \\ 0 & 0 & 0 & .75 & 0 \\ 0 & 0 & 0 & 0 & .5 \end{bmatrix}$$

$$= \begin{bmatrix} 0 & 0 & 0 & 0 & 0 \\ 0 & -.5 & 0 & 0 & 0 \\ 0 & 0 & 0 & 0 & 0 \\ 0 & 0 & 0 & -.25 & 0 \\ 0 & 0 & 0 & 0 & .5 \end{bmatrix}.$$

Using this matrix, we have

$$PV = AQ\,[AP - SP]$$

$$= [4950, 3100, 2050, 500, 4600] \begin{bmatrix} 0 & 0 & 0 & 0 & 0 \\ 0 & -.5 & 0 & 0 & 0 \\ 0 & 0 & 0 & 0 & 0 \\ 0 & 0 & 0 & -.25 & 0 \\ 0 & 0 & 0 & 0 & .5 \end{bmatrix}$$

$$= [0, -1550, 0, -125, 2300].$$

Because of the way we have arranged actual and standard terms, favorable variances show as negative amounts and unfavorable variances are positive.

For calculational convenience in computing quantity variances, we will form the difference vector $[AQ - b[SQ]]$ as follows:

$$[AQ - b[SQ]] = [4950, 3100, 2050, 500, 4600] - 1000[5, 3, 2, .5, 4]$$
$$= [4950, 3100, 2050, 500, 4600] - [5000, 3000, 2000, 500, 4000]$$
$$= [-50, 100, 50, 0, 600].$$

Using this vector, we have

$$QV = [AQ - b[SQ]] \cdot SP$$

$$= [-50, \ 100, \ 50, \ 0, \ 600] \cdot \begin{bmatrix} 1 & 0 & 0 & 0 & 0 \\ 0 & 2.0 & 0 & 0 & 0 \\ 0 & 0 & 2.0 & 0 & 0 \\ 0 & 0 & 0 & .75 & 0 \\ 0 & 0 & 0 & 0 & .5 \end{bmatrix}$$

$$= [-50, \ 200, \ 100, \ 0, \ 300] \ .$$

The other variances required are calculated as follows:

$$\text{total material price variance} = \sum_{k=1}^{2} pv_k = 0 + (-1550) = -1550,$$

$$\text{total labor rate variance} = \sum_{k=3}^{5} pv_k = 0 + (\ \ 125) + 2300 = 2175,$$

$$\text{total material usage variance} = \sum_{k=1}^{2} qv_k = (-50) + 200 = 150,$$

$$\text{total labor efficiency variance} = \sum_{k=3}^{5} qv_k = 100 + 0 + 300 = 400,$$

$$TV = PV + QV = [0, -1550, 0, -125, 2300] + [-50, 200, 100, 0, 300]$$
$$= [-50, -1350, 100, -125, 2600] \ ,$$

$$\text{grand total variance} = tv_. = \sum_{k=1}^{5} tv_k$$

$$= (-50) + (-1350) + 100 + (-125) + 2600$$

$$= 1175.$$

3.4 A REFINEMENT TO REFLECT THE JOINT VARIANCES

Once your study of variance analysis has progressed beyond the elementary level, you will be aware that there is a hidden inconsistency in the two-variance (price and quantity) model presented above. It defines the quantity variance as the difference between actual and standard quantity multiplied by the *standard* price, but it defines the price variance as the difference between actual and standard price multiplied by the *actual* quantity. Since the quantity variance is computed without allowing for price deviations from standard, one can argue that the price variance should not be influenced by deviations from standard quantities either.

If the price variance is computed without regard to quantity deviations, the formula is

$$PV = SQ\left[AP - SP\right].$$

When price and quantity variances are computed in this mutually consistent way, it is necessary to define a third variance which reflects the impact on performance of simultaneous deviations in both prices and quantities. This variance, called the joint variance JV, is computed as follows:

$$JV = \left[AP - SP\right] \cdot \left[AQ - SQ\right].$$

To satisfy yourself that this variance is indeed necessary when the PV vector is defined over standard quantities instead of actual, expand the three variance expressions and cancel out offsetting terms. You will observe that $PV + QV$ no longer equals TV, but that $PV + QV + JV$ does.

The calculation of JV using matrix techniques involves nothing we have not already considered. It is just a matter of multiplying the difference vector $\left[AQ - b\left[SQ\right]\right]$, which we have already used once, times the difference matrix $\left[AP - SP\right]$, which has also already been computed. The result is a five-component row vector, the entries of which, jv_i, represent the joint variances for each manufacturing component. For example, using the numbers presented in the preceding section of the chapter, we have

$$JV = \left[AQ - b\left[SQ\right]\right] \cdot \left[AP - SP\right]$$

$$= \left[-50, 100, 50, 0, 600\right] \cdot \begin{bmatrix} 0 & 0 & 0 & 0 & 0 \\ 0 & -.5 & 0 & 0 & 0 \\ 0 & 0 & 0 & 0 & 0 \\ 0 & 0 & 0 & -.25 & 0 \\ 0 & 0 & 0 & 0 & .5 \end{bmatrix}$$

$$= \left[0, -50, 0, 0, 300\right].$$

The new price-variance vector computed with standard quantities is

$$PV = b[SQ] \cdot [AP - SP]$$

$$= 1000[5, 3, 2, .5, 4] \cdot \begin{bmatrix} 0 & 0 & 0 & 0 & 0 \\ 0 & -.5 & 0 & 0 & 0 \\ 0 & 0 & 0 & 0 & 0 \\ 0 & 0 & 0 & -.25 & 0 \\ 0 & 0 & 0 & 0 & .5 \end{bmatrix}$$

$$= [5000, 3000, 2000, 500, 4000] \cdot \begin{bmatrix} 0 & 0 & 0 & 0 & 0 \\ 0 & -.5 & 0 & 0 & 0 \\ 0 & 0 & 0 & 0 & 0 \\ 0 & 0 & 0 & -.25 & 0 \\ 0 & 0 & 0 & 0 & .5 \end{bmatrix}$$

$$= [0, -1500, 0, -125, 2000].$$

The quantity-variance calculation does not change, nor does the total variance vector TV. To verify this, we observe

$$\begin{aligned} TV &= PV + QV + JV \\ &= [0, -1500, 0, -125, 2000] \\ &\quad + [-50, 200, 100, 0, 300] + [0, -50, 0, 0, 300] \\ &= [-50, -1350, 100, -125, 2600]. \end{aligned}$$

This agrees with the result shown at the end of Section 3.3.

We will conclude this part of the chapter with one more example of a matrix-oriented variance calculation.

3.5 THE VARIANCE SUMMARY MATRIX

Another interesting variation on the use of matrix techniques in setting up variance calculations is the computation of a 2×2 variance summary matrix V, with entries as follows:

$$V = \begin{bmatrix} v_{11} & v_{12} \\ v_{21} & v_{22} \end{bmatrix} = \begin{bmatrix} \text{total standard cost} & \text{total quantity variance} \\ \text{total price variance} & \text{total joint variance} \end{bmatrix}.$$

To achieve this result, we need only set up two matrices involving basic price and quantity data and then perform one matrix multiplication.

Specifically, let P be the $2 \times n$ matrix whose first row represents standard prices for all manufacturing components and whose second row represents the differences between standard and actual prices for the components. Similarly, let Q be the $n \times 2$ matrix whose first column represents standard quantities (at the specified output level) for each of the manufacturing components and whose second column represents the differences between standard and actual quantities for the components. Departing for just a moment from the convention that matrix entries are denoted by the lower-case form of the letter used to denote the matrix itself and substituting instead the price and quantity notation we used in preceding sections of this chapter, we have the following symbolic representation of P and Q:

$$P = \begin{bmatrix} sp_1 & sp_2 \cdots & sp_n \\ (ap_1 - sp_1) & (ap_2 - sp_2) \cdots & (ap_n - sp_n) \end{bmatrix},$$

$$Q = \begin{bmatrix} sq_1 & (aq_1 - sq_1) \\ sq_2 & (aq_2 - sq_2) \\ \vdots & \vdots \\ sq_n & (aq_n - sq_n) \end{bmatrix}.$$

Carrying this notation one step further, you will note that the 2×2 product matrix $P \cdot Q$ can be represented as follows:

$$P \cdot Q = \begin{bmatrix} \sum_{i=1}^{n} sp_i \, sq_i & \sum_{i=1}^{n} sp_i \, (aq_i - sq_i) \\ \sum_{i=1}^{n} sq_i \, (ap_i - sp_i) & \sum_{i=1}^{n} (ap_i - sp_i)(aq_i - sq_i) \end{bmatrix}.$$

You should immediately recognize these expressions as the definitions of total standard cost and each of the three variances. In other words, the product matrix $P \cdot Q$ is the variance summary matrix we earlier called V. More formally, $V = P \cdot Q$.

We can illustrate this idea using the same numbers as in the preceding sections. Specifically,

$$P = \begin{bmatrix} 1. & 2. & 2. & .75 & .5 \\ 0 & -.5 & 0 & -.25 & .5 \end{bmatrix},$$

$$Q = \begin{bmatrix} 5000 & -50 \\ 3000 & 100 \\ 2000 & 50 \\ 500 & 0 \\ 4000 & 600 \end{bmatrix}.$$

Thus the product matrix $P \cdot Q$ is as follows:

$$P \cdot Q = \begin{bmatrix} 17375 & 550 \\ 375 & 250 \end{bmatrix}.$$

You can check that the three variance quantities shown here do in fact represent the sums of the elements in the variance vectors shown at the end of Section 3.4.

We will now turn to the last major section of the chapter, a matrix approach to cost-behavior analysis using linear-regression techniques.

*4. A MATRIX APPROACH TO COST-BEHAVIOR ANALYSIS

4.1 INTRODUCTION

Soon after you begin studying cost behavior, you will undoubtedly become familiar with the formula, $y = a + bx$, for a semivariable cost. In this notation, y refers to the total amount of cost, a to the nonvariable portion, x to the number of units, and b to the variable cost rate per unit. Special cases of the formula also apply to pure variable and pure nonvariable costs as well. Specifically, if $a = 0$ the result is a pure variable cost. Similarly, if $b = 0$ the result is a pure nonvariable cost. Because we will later want to refer to them as elements of a vector, we will replace the symbols a and

---

*This section can be skipped without loss of continuity.

b with b_1 and b_2, respectively. Thus, in this book, the equation will be written $y = b_1 + b_2 x$.

Some elementary accounting textbooks assume for purposes of illustration that this relationship is always perfect. In other words, they assume that if we know x we can compute y exactly by just substituting the known value for x in the equation $y = b_1 + b_2 x$. Most books do acknowledge, however, that the relationship is never perfect in actual situations and that such an equation is really only an approximation. In actual cases, b_1 and b_2 are not known. One can directly observe past values of x and y, but the problem is to estimate b_1 and b_2 so that y can be predicted for any given future output level x.

Those books which are concerned with applying this idea, called fixed/variable cost analysis, to real-world situations usually suggest the "method of least squares" as the most scientific, yet still operational, way of estimating b_1 and b_2. This segment of the chapter deals with the least-squares method in a matrix framework.

4.2 THE SINGLE-VARIABLE LEAST-SQUARES MODEL

Whenever given estimates of b_1 and b_2, say b'_1 and b'_2, are used to estimate y, there will be some error in the estimate. If y' is our estimate of y, the error e is the difference $y - y'$. In accounting examples, this error is most likely to result because x and y are not really related in a perfectly linear way, or because factors other than quantity produced x also affect cost y. It is usually not due to error in measuring either x or y. For purposes of this book, in fact, we will assume that measurement error is not a problem at all. Since y' is calculated from the equation $y' = b'_1 + b'_2 x$, another way of expressing the error term is

$$e = y - y' = y - (b'_1 + b'_2 x).$$

If we have n observed values x_i, each time we use one to estimate y_i we will have a corresponding error term e_i.

Since some values y'_i may be greater than the true y_i and some may be less, some of the e_i's will be positive and some negative. If these errors are squared and then summed, the result is a nonnegative quantity which varies in magnitude directly with the precision of the estimates y'_i. Each different combination of b'_1 and b'_2 will yield a different set of values y'_i for a given set of values x_i, and thus will yield a different sum of squared errors. The method of least squares is a way of choosing b'_1 and b'_2 so that the sum of squared errors is minimized. Because they result in the lowest possible value for the error-squares sum, the so-called least-squares estimates b'_1 and b'_2 represent the most precise way we have of estimating y_i for a given x_i.

Calculationally, the least-squares estimates b'_1 and b'_2 are the values which satisfy the following set of two simultaneous equations:*

$$b'_1 n + b'_2 \Sigma x_i = \Sigma y_i, \tag{7}$$

$$b'_1 \Sigma x_i + b'_2 \Sigma x_i^2 = \Sigma x_i y_i. \tag{8}$$

Since we know n and can compute Σx_i, Σx_i^2, Σy_i and $\Sigma x_i y_i$, computing b'_1 and b'_2 is just a matter of substituting these quantities into equations (7) and (8) and then solving the so-called "normal" equations simultaneously. For example, assume that we observe the set of x and y values shown below.

x	y
1	5.5
2	6.8
3	9.2

The key quantities needed to calculate the least-squares estimators are

$$\Sigma x_i = 1 + 2 + 3 = 6,$$

$$\Sigma x_i^2 = 1 + 4 + 9 = 14,$$

$$\Sigma y_i = 5.5 + 6.8 + 9.2 = 21.5,$$

$$\Sigma x_i y_i = 1(5.5) + 2(6.8) + 3(9.2) = 46.7.$$

Using these values, we are looking for b'_1 and b'_2 which satisfy the following two equations:

$$b'_1 \cdot 3 + b'_2 \cdot 6 = 21.5, \tag{9}$$

$$b'_1 \cdot 6 + b'_2 \cdot 14 = 46.7. \tag{10}$$

---

*Students who have studied partial derivatives in elementary calculus will recognize this set of equations as the partial derivatives of the expression Σe_i^2 or $\Sigma (y_i - (b'_1 + b'_2 x_i))^2$, first for b'_1 and then for b'_2, each set equal to zero. This is, of course, the standard approach to minimizing an equation in two unknowns.

4.3 A MATRIX INTERPRETATION OF THE MODEL

Although it is not exactly obvious, you should be able to satisfy yourself that this set of equations can be expressed as the following matrix equation:

$$A \cdot B' = C,$$

where

B' is the vector of unknowns $\begin{bmatrix} b'_1 \\ b'_2 \end{bmatrix}$,

A is the coefficient matrix $\begin{bmatrix} 3 & 6 \\ 6 & 14 \end{bmatrix}$,   and

C is the vector $\begin{bmatrix} 21.5 \\ 46.7 \end{bmatrix}$.

It is good practice in the mechanics of matrix multiplication to verify for yourself that the expression $A \cdot B' = C$, is just another way of writing the set of normal equations shown above.

To solve this matrix equation for B', we first note that premultiplying both sides by A^{-1} results in the following:

$$A^{-1}[A \cdot B'] = A^{-1} \cdot C.$$

Using property 2 from Chapter 1, we have

$$[A^{-1} \cdot A]B' = A^{-1} \cdot C.$$

Remembering that $A^{-1} \cdot A = I$ and that $I \cdot B' = B'$, we can write

$$B' = A^{-1} \cdot C.$$

Since A^{-1} can be computed and C is known, this last expression is in a form which yields readily calculable values for b'_1 and b'_2. Specifically, we can verify that

$$A^{-1} = \begin{bmatrix} \frac{7}{3} & -1 \\ -1 & \frac{1}{2} \end{bmatrix},$$

so that we have

$$B' = A^{-1} \cdot C = \begin{bmatrix} \frac{7}{3} & -1 \\ -1 & \frac{1}{2} \end{bmatrix} \cdot \begin{bmatrix} 21.5 \\ 46.7 \end{bmatrix} = \begin{bmatrix} 3.5 \\ 1.85 \end{bmatrix}.$$

Using these values, we note that $b_1' + b_2' x$ is never exactly equal to y because x and y are not related in a perfectly linear way. The errors when using these estimates can be summarized as in Table 3.1.

Table 3.1

x_i	y_i	$y_i' = b_1' + b_2' x_i = 3.5 + 1.85x_i$	$e_i = y_i - y_i'$
1	5.5	5.35	.15
2	6.8	7.2	−.40
3	9.2	9.05	.15

In this example, the resulting sum of error squares is equal to $(.15)^2 + (-.40)^2 + (.15)^2$ or .205. Because we estimated b_1 and b_2 using the method of least squares, we can be assured that no other pair of coefficient estimates would yield as small a sum of error squares.

Summarizing our progress so far, we have seen that the "best" estimate* we can make of b_1 and b_2 when we are given a series of x and y values is found by calculating Σx_i, Σx_i^2, Σy_i, and $\Sigma x_i y_i$, substituting these values in the "normal" equations, Eqs. 7 and 8, and then solving these equations using the matrix inversion approach. This procedure was illustrated in the immediately preceding paragraphs.

Although this procedure is straightforward and always leads to an estimate which is "best" in a least-squares sense, it is more cumbersome than necessary. Making further use of matrix techniques, we can combine the steps before the matrix inversion with the inversion step itself to get a more direct calculational approach. We first take a closer look at the normal equations:

$$b_1' n + b_2' \Sigma x_i = \Sigma y_i, \tag{7}$$

$$b_1' \Sigma x_i + b_2' \Sigma x_i^2 = \Sigma x_i y_i. \tag{8}$$

---

*It is "best" because it minimizes the sum of error squares. It also turns out to be the "best" estimate in a formal statistical sense, but that is beyond the scope of this book.

We can rewrite them in matrix equation form as follows:

$$\begin{bmatrix} n & \Sigma x_i \\ \Sigma x_i & \Sigma x_i^2 \end{bmatrix} \cdot \begin{bmatrix} b'_1 \\ b'_2 \end{bmatrix} = \begin{bmatrix} \Sigma y_i \\ \Sigma x_i y_i \end{bmatrix}.$$

At this point we will make one of those jumps for which mathematics books are notorious. The classic lead-in is the statement "It is obvious that. . . ." In most cases, what follows the lead-in is not only not obvious, but actually represents a brilliant insight whose original discovery quite probably grew out of very extensive and intensive reflection on the problem at hand. Our next step certainly falls in this category of "Aha!" discoveries. Although it is not obvious, you should be able to verify that it is true. Specifically making use of the "transpose" operation, we will transform the matrix equation:

$$\begin{bmatrix} n & \Sigma x_i \\ \Sigma x_i & \Sigma x_i^2 \end{bmatrix} \cdot \begin{bmatrix} b'_1 \\ b'_2 \end{bmatrix} = \begin{bmatrix} \Sigma y_i \\ \Sigma x_i y_i \end{bmatrix}$$

by writing $[X^TX]B' = X^TY$, where

$$X \text{ is the } n \times 2 \text{ matrix } \begin{bmatrix} 1 & x_1 \\ 1 & x_2 \\ . & . \\ \vdots & \vdots \\ 1 & x_n \end{bmatrix},$$

$$B' \text{ is the vector } \begin{bmatrix} b'_1 \\ b'_2 \end{bmatrix}, \text{ and}$$

$$Y \text{ is the vector } \begin{bmatrix} y_1 \\ y_2 \\ . \\ \vdots \\ y_n \end{bmatrix}.$$

To help verify this result we will set it up in full detail using the X matrix and the B' and Y vectors:

$$[X^TX]B' = X^TY,$$

or

$$\begin{bmatrix} 1 & 1 & \ldots & 1 \\ x_1 & x_2 & \ldots & x_n \end{bmatrix} \cdot \begin{bmatrix} 1 & x_1 \\ 1 & x_2 \\ \vdots & \vdots \\ 1 & x_n \end{bmatrix} \cdot \begin{bmatrix} b' \\ b_2 \end{bmatrix} = \begin{bmatrix} 1 & 1 & \ldots & 1 \\ x_1 & x_2 & \ldots & x_n \end{bmatrix} \cdot \begin{bmatrix} y_1 \\ y_2 \\ \vdots \\ y_n \end{bmatrix}.$$

Performing the indicated multiplications, it should now be clear that the result is the normal equations

$$\begin{bmatrix} n & \Sigma x_i \\ \Sigma x_i & \Sigma x_i^2 \end{bmatrix} \cdot \begin{bmatrix} b_1' \\ b_2 \end{bmatrix} = \begin{bmatrix} \Sigma y_i \\ \Sigma x_i y_i \end{bmatrix}.$$

Using the streamlined form of the normal equations, $[X^TX]B' = X^TY$, we can easily move to the next step and write

$$R' = [X^TX]^{-1}X^TY.$$

This result comes from pre-multiplying both sides of the equation by $[X^TX]^{-1}$ and then simplifying. In this form, B' is expressed only in terms of combinations of the basic observations, x_i and y_i. It is thus directly calculable. Although one still has to go through all the same individual calculations to solve the problem by hand, the streamlined form greatly facilitates computerization of the process in large-scale problems which are not feasible to undertake manually. It also facilitates the proof of many of the important statistical properties of least-squares estimates which give the approach its widespread applicability; however, the exposition of these properties is beyond the scope of this book.

4.4 AN ILLUSTRATION OF THE SINGLE-VARIABLE MODEL

We will now turn to a cost-analysis example to illustrate the use of the streamlined calculational approach. The problem is to estimate the total cost for a subassembly department of an electronics components manu-

Table 3.2

Period	Total cost	Output
1	$ 7950	1000 units
2	$ 8380	1200 units
3	$ 11125	1500 units
4	$ 6900	800 units
5	$ 7405	1000 units

facturer. The department assembles radar tuning units for inclusion in aircraft tracking equipment produced for the Defense Department. The department employs nine assemblers and one foreman on a one-shift basis. The assemblers are paid on a very complicated piece-rate basis and the foreman is on straight salary. Table 3.2 presents actual total cost and output data for a recent five-month period considered by management to be representative of normal operations.

The cost total covers all items directly chargeable to the department but does not include an allocation from general corporate overhead. The controller wants to develop a simple cost-behavior formula for the department for use in cash-flow budgeting, in preparing pro forma financial statements, and in reviewing operating results quickly with respect to cost-control performance. Output is based on weekly release orders against a long-term, fixed-price contract. The controller expects it to fluctuate between 1000 and 1500 units a month over the next quarter, averaging about 1400 units per month.

Since a semivariable equation of the form $y = b_1 + b_2 x$ is the simplest formula which allows for the fact that total cost is based partly on production volume and partly on items which don't vary as production does, the controller decides to use such a formula for this subassembly department. Furthermore, he decides to use a least-square approach in estimating the formula, based on the data in the preceding table. He sets up the basic components of the computation as follows:

$$X = \begin{bmatrix} 1 & 1000 \\ 1 & 1200 \\ 1 & 1500 \\ 1 & 800 \\ 1 & 1000 \end{bmatrix}, \quad Y = \begin{bmatrix} 7950 \\ 8380 \\ 11125 \\ 6900 \\ 7405 \end{bmatrix}.$$

Using these components, he makes the following computations:

$$X^TX = \begin{bmatrix} 1 & 1 & 1 & 1 & 1 \\ 1000 & 1200 & 1500 & 800 & 1000 \end{bmatrix} \cdot \begin{bmatrix} 1 & 1000 \\ 1 & 1200 \\ 1 & 1500 \\ 1 & 800 \\ 1 & 1000 \end{bmatrix} = \begin{bmatrix} 5 & 5500 \\ 5,500 & 6,330,000 \end{bmatrix},$$

$$X^TY = \begin{bmatrix} 1 & 1 & 1 & 1 & 1 \\ 1000 & 1200 & 1500 & 800 & 1000 \end{bmatrix} \cdot \begin{bmatrix} 7950 \\ 8380 \\ 11125 \\ 6900 \\ 7405 \end{bmatrix} = \begin{bmatrix} 41760 \\ 47,618,500 \end{bmatrix}.$$

His next step is as follows:

$$[X^TX]^{-1} = \begin{bmatrix} 5 & 5500 \\ 5500 & 6,330,000 \end{bmatrix}^{-1} = \cdots = \begin{bmatrix} \dfrac{633}{140} & \dfrac{-11}{2800} \\ \dfrac{-11}{2800} & \dfrac{1}{280,000} \end{bmatrix},$$

He can then compute B' as follows:

$$B' = [X^TX]^{-1}[X^TY] = \begin{bmatrix} \dfrac{633}{140} & \dfrac{-11}{2800} \\ \dfrac{-11}{2800} & \dfrac{1}{280.000} \end{bmatrix} \begin{bmatrix} 41760 \\ 47,618,500 \end{bmatrix} = \begin{bmatrix} 1742 \\ 6.4 \end{bmatrix}.$$

The desired cost-approximating formula is thus $1742 + 6.4(x)$, where x is the number of units produced.

    The controller knows that this is the best possible estimating equation of the form $y = b_1 + b_2 x$. He is bothered, however, by the fact that the estimating error is as large as 12% in one case and 9% in another. He compiles Table 3.3 in considering the overall accuracy of the estimates generated by the least-squares equation.

Table 3.3

Period	Output	Total cost	Estimated cost $= b'_1 + b'_2 x$	Error	% error
1	1000	$ 7950	$ 8142	$ −192	2.4%
2	1200	8380	9422	−1042	12.5%
3	1500	11125	11342	−217	2.0%
4	800	6900	6867	33	.5%
5	1000	7405	8142	−737	9.1%

Overall, the results seem fairly accurate, but the two substantial deviations (periods 2 and 5) and the fact that the equation seems to consistently overestimate total cost (4 periods out of 5) lead the controller to wonder if the equation is really good enough for his purposes.

4.5 A TEST OF ESTIMATING ACCURACY

We have already noted that it is only an approximation to consider that cost is strictly a function of units produced. Many factors other than production volume can influence the level of cost incurrence, such as the size of production runs, the level of employee training and morale, the condition of capital equipment, or even the weather. Although we want to approximate cost behavior by as simple an equation as possible, we don't want to oversimplify the description of the relationship to the extent that the results are meaningless.

One measure of the extent to which a least-squares estimating equation does account for variability in the dependent variables is the correlation coefficient R^2 for the equation. This indicator is computed as follows:

$$R^2 = 1 - \frac{\Sigma e_i^2}{\Sigma y_i^2}.$$

Since the error terms e_i represent the deviations between actual values y_i and estimated values y'_i, the correlation coefficient is really just the percentage of the total variation in y which is explained by the estimating equation. Thus R^2 must be a number between zero and one. The closer the number is to one, the "better" the estimating equation in the sense of explaining the variation in y. We can calculate R^2 for the preceding example as follows:

$$\Sigma y_i = (7950)^2 + (8380)^2 + (11125)^2 + (6900)^2 + (7405)^2 = 357,800,000,$$

$$\Sigma e_i^2 = (-192)^2 + (1042)^2 + (-217)^2 + (33)^2 + (-737)^2 = 1,712,000,$$

$$R^2 = 1 - \frac{1,712,000}{357,800,000} = 1 - .005 = .995.$$

This indicates that the controller's fears are unwarranted, and that the estimating equation is really extremely accurate.

In many cases, however, an estimating equation based on only one explanatory variable is just not adequate. Consider, for example, the following situation:

x_i	y_i
2	95
3	13
1	109
2	25
1	7

For this set of data we have:

$$X^TX = \begin{bmatrix} n & \Sigma x_i \\ \Sigma x_i & \Sigma e_i^2 \end{bmatrix} = \begin{bmatrix} 5 & 9 \\ 9 & 19 \end{bmatrix},$$

$$(X^TX)^{-1} = \begin{bmatrix} 5 & 9 \\ 9 & 19 \end{bmatrix}^{-1} = \begin{bmatrix} \frac{19}{14} & \frac{-9}{14} \\ \frac{-9}{14} & \frac{5}{14} \end{bmatrix},$$

$$X^TY = \begin{bmatrix} \Sigma y_i \\ \Sigma x_i y_i \end{bmatrix} = \begin{bmatrix} 249 \\ 395 \end{bmatrix},$$

$$B' = (X^TX)^{-1}X^TY = \begin{bmatrix} \frac{19}{14} & \frac{-9}{14} \\ \frac{-9}{14} & \frac{5}{14} \end{bmatrix} \cdot \begin{bmatrix} 249 \\ 395 \end{bmatrix} = \begin{bmatrix} 84 \\ -19 \end{bmatrix}.$$

Table 3.4.

x_i	y_i	$y_i' = 84 - 19x_i$	e_i	% error
2	95	46	49	51.5%
3	13	27	-14	107%
1	109	65	44	40.5%
2	25	46	-21	84%
1	7	65	-58	830%

Table 3.4 summarizes estimating accuracy for this example.

Clearly, this equation is not of much use in estimating y. In fact, the equation only explains about 60% of the variation in y, as the following calculation shows:

$$\Sigma e_i^2 = (49)^2 + (-14)^2 + (44)^2 + (-21)^2 + (-58)^2 = 8299,$$

$$\Sigma y_i^2 = (95)^2 + (13)^2 + (109)^2 + (25)^2 + (7)^2 = 21749,$$

$$R^2 = 1 - \Sigma e_i^2 \Big/ \Sigma y_i^2 = 1 - \frac{8299}{21749} = 1 - .38 = .62.$$

4.6 EXPANDING THE MODEL: THE TWO-VARIABLE CASE

In cases like this, the estimating equation must be expanded if it is to be of any real use. Although we could still focus on a single explanatory variable x, and attempt to relate it to y by means of a more complicated functional form than a straight line, the mathematics of developing estimating equations becomes very difficult to handle as soon as the assumption of linearity is relaxed. Thus the first thing we try to do is find a second explanatory variable which can be included with the first one in a two-variable linear equation of the form

$$y = b_0 + b_1 x_1 + b_2 x_2.$$

If such a variable can be found, the problem can be dealt with in exactly the same form as the single-variable case.

The matrix X now becomes $3 \times n$, with the first column still all ones, the second column arraying the values of the variable x_1, and the third column arraying x_2. The vector B' is now 3×1:

$$B' = \begin{bmatrix} b'_0 \\ b'_1 \\ b'_2 \end{bmatrix}.$$

The vector Y is still $n \times 1$, representing the observed values y_i. The normal equations can still be written as $[X^TX]B' = X^TY$, and B' can still be computed from the expression $B' = [X^TX]^{-1}X^TY$. In other words, this matrix format is completely generalizable to as many different explanatory variables as one chooses to include, as long as all the variables are linked in a linear equation of the form

$$y = b_0 + b_1x_1 + b_2x_2 + \cdots + b_mx_m.$$

If the single-variable estimating equation $y = b_0 + b_1x_1$ is inadequate, therefore, the problem is simply to expand the equation, maintaining the linear form, until one gets an equation for which R^2 is "high enough."

To illustrate how adding a second variable can dramatically improve the explanatory power of an estimating equation, let us return to the preceding example. This time we will relate y to two separate variables, x_1 and x_2:

x_1	x_2	y
2	10	95
3	2	13
1	11	109
2	3	25
1	1	7

We will solve for an estimating equation of the form $y = b_0 + b_1x_1 + b_2x_2$. The procedure, with which you should now be familiar, is as follows.

1. $$X = \begin{bmatrix} 1 & 2 & 10 \\ 1 & 3 & 2 \\ 1 & 1 & 11 \\ 1 & 2 & 3 \\ 1 & 1 & 1 \end{bmatrix}, \qquad Y = \begin{bmatrix} 95 \\ 13 \\ 109 \\ 25 \\ 7 \end{bmatrix}.$$

2. $[X^TX] = \begin{bmatrix} 1 & 1 & 1 & 1 & 1 \\ 2 & 3 & 1 & 2 & 1 \\ 10 & 2 & 11 & 3 & 1 \end{bmatrix} \cdot \begin{bmatrix} 1 & 2 & 10 \\ 1 & 3 & 2 \\ 1 & 1 & 11 \\ 1 & 2 & 3 \\ 1 & 1 & 1 \end{bmatrix} = \begin{bmatrix} 5 & 9 & 27 \\ 9 & 9 & 44 \\ 27 & 44 & 235 \end{bmatrix}$

3. $[X^TX]^{-1} = \begin{bmatrix} 5 & 9 & 27 \\ 9 & 19 & 44 \\ 27 & 44 & 235 \end{bmatrix}^{-1} = \begin{bmatrix} 2.22 & -.82 & -.10 \\ -.82 & .39 & .02 \\ -.10 & .02 & .01 \end{bmatrix}$.

4. $X^TY = \begin{bmatrix} 1 & 1 & 1 & 1 & 1 \\ 2 & 3 & 1 & 2 & 1 \\ 10 & 2 & 11 & 3 & 1 \end{bmatrix} \cdot \begin{bmatrix} 95 \\ 13 \\ 109 \\ 25 \\ 7 \end{bmatrix} = \begin{bmatrix} 249 \\ 395 \\ 2257 \end{bmatrix}$.

5. $B' = [X^TX]^{-1}X^TY = \begin{bmatrix} 2.22 & -.82 & -.10 \\ -.82 & .39 & .02 \\ -.10 & .02 & .01 \end{bmatrix} \cdot \begin{bmatrix} 249 \\ 395 \\ 2257 \end{bmatrix} = \begin{bmatrix} 26 \\ -5 \\ 6 \end{bmatrix}$.

The desired estimating equation thus becomes

$$y' = 26 - 5x_1 + 6x_2.$$

Using the same format as above, Table 3.5 summarizes estimating accuracy.

We can thus compute the new R^2 as follows:

$$\Sigma e_i^2 = (19)^2 + (-10)^2 + (22)^2 + (-9)^2 + (-20)^2 = 1426,$$

$$\Sigma y_i^2 = (95)^2 + (13)^2 + (109)^2 + (25)^2 + (7)^2 = 21749,$$

Table 3.5

y_i	$y'_i = b'_0 + b'_1 x_1 + b'_2 x_2$	$e_i = y_i - y'_i$	% error
95	76	19	20%
13	23	−10	77%
109	87	22	20.2%
25	34	−9	36%
7	27	−20	237%

$$R^2 = 1 - \Sigma e_i^2 / \Sigma y_i^2$$

$$= 1 - 1426/21749$$

$$= 1 - .066 = .934.$$

Instead of 62%, the estimating equation now explains 93% of the variability in y.

Although it is not usually possible to find two x variables which can be combined in a linear estimating equation to explain this high a percentage of cost variability in actual applications, values as high as .7 to .8 are often possible if the set of x variables is expanded to as many as six or seven. As noted above, such an extension does not alter the calculational technique at all. It just expands the size of the matrices, $[X^TX]$, B', and X^TY. As long as there are at least two to three times as many observations as there are explanatory variables in the estimating equation, the least-squares technique can be counted on to produce a statistically sound estimating equation.

4.7 A COST-ANALYSIS EXAMPLE OF THE TWO-VARIABLE MODEL

We will conclude the chapter with another cost-analysis example, this time involving two independent variables. We want to develop a cost estimating equation for the machine-shop department of an industrial pump manufacturing company. The machine shop carries out the preliminary grinding, boring, and tapping operations on pump-housing castings before they are transferred to the assembly department. Some of the castings are grey iron and the rest are stainless steel, depending on the intended use for the finished pump. The machining time varies significantly between grey-iron and stainless-steel housings. Also, different equipment in the department is used for the different metals. The same machinists work on both types of castings, but they are paid different piece rates for the two types because of the differences in processing time.

The department has some expenses which are unrelated to the volume of output, some expenses which are related to the output of grey-iron housings and some related to the output of stainless-steel housings. We will thus use an estimating equation of the form

$$y = b_0 + b_1 x_1 + b_2 x_2.$$

The data upon which the equation will be based are taken from the past nine months' actual cost and output results for the department. Management considers these months to be representative of normal departmental operations. The data are shown in Table 3.6.

For purposes of computing B', the relevant quantities are

$$X = \begin{bmatrix} 1 & 5 & 3 \\ 1 & 5 & 6 \\ 1 & 5 & 12 \\ 1 & 10 & 3 \\ 1 & 10 & 6 \\ 1 & 10 & 12 \\ 1 & 15 & 3 \\ 1 & 15 & 6 \\ 1 & 15 & 12 \end{bmatrix}, \quad [X^TX] = \begin{bmatrix} 9 & 90 & 63 \\ 90 & 1050 & 630 \\ 63 & 630 & 567 \end{bmatrix}, \quad X^TY = \begin{bmatrix} 210 \\ 2230 \\ 1602 \end{bmatrix}.$$

We leave it for you to verify that

$$B' = [X^TX]^{-1}X^TY = \begin{bmatrix} 9 & 90 & 63 \\ 90 & 1050 & 630 \\ 63 & 630 & 567 \end{bmatrix}^{-1} \cdot \begin{bmatrix} 210 \\ 2230 \\ 1602 \end{bmatrix} = \cdots = \begin{bmatrix} 7.333 \\ .867 \\ 1.048 \end{bmatrix}.$$

In reading this result, remember that y was given in thousands and both x_1 and x_2 in hundreds. With this in mind, we can interpret the result to

Table 3.6.

Month	Departmental cost (in thousands)	Grey-iron housings processed (in hundreds)	Stainless-steel housings processed (in hundreds)
January 1971	$16	5	3
February	16	5	6
March	27	5	12
April	18	10	3
May	20	10	6
June	28	10	12
July	26	15	3
August	27	15	6
September	32	15	12

mean that our estimate of machine-shop cost each month is equal to $7333 plus $86.70 for each grey-iron housing processed and $104.80 for each stainless-steel housing. We also leave it to you to verify that R^2 for this estimating equation is equal to .903. As a hint, remember that $R^2 = 1 - \Sigma e_i^2 / \Sigma y_i^2$, and that a table like Table 3.5 is helpful in computing the values e_i.

SELECTED REFERENCES

1. Benston, George. "Multiple Regression Analysis of Cost Behavior," *The Accounting Review*, October 1966.
2. Chiu, John, and Don DeCoster. "Multiple Product Costing by Multiple Correlation Analysis," *The Accounting Review*, October 1966.
3. Churchill, Neil. "Linear Algebra and Cost Allocation: Some Examples," *The Accounting Review*, October 1964.
4. Comiskey, Eugene. "Cost Control by Regression Analysis," *The Accounting Review*, April 1966.
5. Corcoran, A. Wayne. "A Proposal for Condensing Diverse Accounting Procedures," *Management Services*, November-December 1966.
6. Corcoran, A. Wayne. "A Matrix Approach to Process Cost Reporting," *Management Accounting*, November 1966.
7. Corcoran, A. Wayne. *Mathematical Applications in Accounting*. Harcourt, Brace & World, New York, 1968. Especially Chapter 7.
8. Drebin, Allan. "The Inventory Calculus," *Journal of Accounting Research*, Spring 1966.

9. Frank, Werner, and Rene Manes. "A Standard Cost Application of Matrix Algebra," *The Accounting Review*, July 1967.
10. Jones, Gardner. "Linear Algebra for the Neophyte," *The Accounting Review*, July 1965.
11. Livingstone, John Leslie. *Management Planning and Control: Mathematical Models*. McGraw-Hill, New York, 1970. Especially Parts 1–2 and 2–2.
12. Livingstone, John Leslie. "Matrix Algebra and Cost Allocation," *The Accounting Review*, July 1968.
13. Manes, Rene. "Comment on Matrix Theory and Cost Allocation," *The Accounting Review*, July 1965.
14. Williams, Thomas, and Charles Griffin. "Matrix Theory and Cost Allocation," *The Accounting Review*, July 1964.

Chapter Four

MATRIX APPLICATIONS
IN FINANCIAL ACCOUNTING

1. INTRODUCTION

In this chapter we will consider five problems related to financial accounting which are usually covered in intermediate accounting courses. Three of them, dealing with balance sheet valuation, will be treated as a unit. This treatment involves three variations on the use of a probability model based on matrix methods. Since the use of formal probability models is as much a departure from conventional practice in accounting as the use of matrix techniques, we will explain the model to be used in some detail and also discuss briefly its relevance to the valuation problem.

Before tackling this subject, however, we will consider two matrix applications which involve nothing conceptually new, only an improvement in calculational procedures.

2. THE TAX, BONUS, PROFIT-SHARING CONTRIBUTION PROBLEM

At one time or another all accountants are called upon to calculate a set of quantities related in such a way that each of them requires that all the others be known. This is somewhat troublesome when only two variables are involved, such as a "floating" rent expense depending on profit after deducting payroll bonuses, and payroll bonuses depending on profit after deducting rent expense. In such cases, however, it is usually possible to "muddle through," by trial and error if nothing else. When more than two simultaneously interdependent quantities are involved, though, trial and error can be a frustrating process. We will illustrate here an approach, based on matrix methods, for solving such problems directly and precisely.

Consider a situation in which federal income-tax expense is to be computed after deducting payroll bonuses and the contribution to the profit-sharing plan. Payroll bonuses, however, are based on income after deducting profit-sharing contribution and federal income-tax. Finally, the profit-sharing contribution is based on income after deducting bonuses and taxes. Also assume that the tax rate is 50%, the bonus rate 10%, the profit-sharing contribution 5%, and that profit, before considering any of the three interdependent items, is $5,000,000.

To solve this problem, we will first define three variables:

$$x_1 = \text{tax expense},$$
$$x_2 = \text{bonus expense},$$
$$x_3 = \text{profit-sharing contribution expense}.$$

The next step is to describe their interrelationships formally in a set of "simultaneous equations." The term "simultaneous equations" simply means that what is treated as a "known" in some equations is an "unknown" in others, and vice versa. The set of equations for the example at hand is as follows:

$$x_1 = .5(5,000,000 - x_2 - x_3) = 2,500,000 - .5x_2 - .5x_3,$$
$$x_2 = .1(5,000,000 - x_1 - x_3) = 500,000 - .1x_1 - .1x_3,$$
$$x_3 = .05(5,000,000 - x_1 - x_2) = 250,000 - .05x_1 - .05x_2.$$

We can rearrange these equations in the following more symmetric form:

$$x_1 + .5x_2 + .5x_3 = 2,500,000,$$
$$.1x_1 + x_2 + .1x_3 = 500,000,$$
$$.05x_1 + .05x_2 = x_3 = 250,000.$$

From here, it is a short jump to convert the set of equations to matrix form:

$$\begin{bmatrix} 1.0 & 0.5 & 0.5 \\ 0.1 & 1.0 & 0.1 \\ 0.05 & 0.05 & 1.0 \end{bmatrix} \cdot \begin{bmatrix} x_1 \\ x_2 \\ x_3 \end{bmatrix} = \begin{bmatrix} 2,500,000 \\ 500,000 \\ 250,000 \end{bmatrix}.$$

Using the matrix inversion technique presented in the preceding chapter, we can now write the following expression for the solution vector X.

$$X = \begin{bmatrix} x_1 \\ x_2 \\ x_3 \end{bmatrix} = \begin{bmatrix} 1.0 & 0.5 & 0.5 \\ 0.1 & 1.0 & 0.1 \\ 0.05 & 0.05 & 1.0 \end{bmatrix}^{-1} \cdot \begin{bmatrix} 2,500,000 \\ 500,000 \\ 250,000 \end{bmatrix}.$$

Using row operations, you can satisfy yourself that

$$\begin{bmatrix} 1.0 & 0.5 & 0.5 \\ 0.1 & 1.0 & 0.1 \\ 0.05 & 0.05 & 1.0 \end{bmatrix}^{-1} = \begin{bmatrix} 1.075 & -.513 & -.486 \\ -.103 & 1.052 & -.054 \\ -.049 & -.025 & 1.028 \end{bmatrix}.$$

Thus we have

$$X = \begin{bmatrix} x_1 \\ x_2 \\ x_3 \end{bmatrix} = \begin{bmatrix} 1.075 & -.513 & -.486 \\ -.103 & 1.052 & -.054 \\ -.049 & -.025 & 1.028 \end{bmatrix} \cdot \begin{bmatrix} 2,500,000 \\ 500,000 \\ 250,000 \end{bmatrix} - \begin{bmatrix} 2,313,000 \\ 256,000 \\ 121,000 \end{bmatrix}.$$

You should recognize this technique as the same one we used in solving the so-called "normal" equations in Chapter 3. It is a very useful technique in any situation which can be expressed as a set of n simultaneous algebraic equations in n unknowns. Although our present example involves three unknowns, the approach is also applicable to two-variable problems and to those involving more than three variables.

3. THE DEPRECIATION LAPSE SCHEDULE

A common problem in accounting is to prepare a schedule for a set of fixed-asset items showing the depreciation expense to be booked in each year for each item. Such a schedule, shown in Table 4.1, is useful in tax planning, in forecasting cash flow, and in projecting future financial statements. Although the schedule is useful enough to be worth preparing, the preparation itself is not a very interesting or stimulating task. It is thus a prime candidate for systemization, so that it can be completed as quickly as possible. Rather than working out the calculations for each item separately and then summarizing the results, as in Table 4.1, we can structure the entire set of calculations in matrix form. This provides a more convenient format for performing the calculations if they must be

Table 4.1.

Years	1	2	3	4	5	6	7	8	. . .	n	Total
Items											
A											
B											
C											
D											
.											
Total											

done manually, and also represents the most efficient framework for computerizing the process.

The elements of the matrix approach are as follows.

1. A row vector C of original-cost numbers for each fixed asset item:

$$C = [c_1\ c_2\ c_3\ \dots\ c_m].$$

2. A diagonal "depreciation-base" matrix B, the main diagonal elements of which, b_{ii}, represent cost minus salvage value, stated as a percentage of cost, for each item:

$$B = \begin{bmatrix} b_{11} & 0 & 0 & 0 & \dots & 0 \\ 0 & b_{22} & 0 & 0 & \dots & 0 \\ . & . & & & & . \\ . & & & & & . \\ 0 & 0 & 0 & 0 & \dots & b_{mm} \end{bmatrix}.$$

3. A depreciation-rate matrix R, the ith row of which represents the fraction of the depreciation base to be expensed for the ith asset item in each year of its life. If some assets have longer lives than others, R must have as many columns as the longest-lived asset. If the asset represented in row i has only a five-year life but R has eight columns, put zeroes in positions r_{i6}, r_{i7}, and r_{i8}.

$$R = \begin{bmatrix} r_{11} & r_{12} & \dots & r_{1n} \\ r_{21} & r_{22} & \dots & r_{2n} \\ . & & & . \\ . & & & . \\ r_{m1} & r_{m2} & \dots & r_{mn} \end{bmatrix},$$

where $\sum_{k=1}^{n} r_{ik} = 1$ for $i = 1, 2, \ldots, m$.

These requirements conform to the usual information related to depreciation accounting in most companies. Original cost of each asset is certainly basic information readily available and normally collected. The matrices B and R just represent a more formal way of recording the company's so-called "depreciation policy," which typically covers, for each type of asset purchased, the following information:

1. Estimated length of life
2. Estimated salvage-value percentage
3. Depreciation method.

For example, assume that a company using "composite" depreciation methods maintains five classes of fixed assets:

1. Leasehold improvements
2. Manufacturing equipment
3. Delivery trucks
4. Office furniture and fixtures
5. Salesmen's autos.

The depreciation policy for each class of assets is shown in Table 4.2.

Using the information in the salvage column, we can construct the following matrix B:

$$B = \begin{bmatrix} 1.0 & 0 & 0 & 0 & 0 \\ 0 & .80 & 0 & 0 & 0 \\ 0 & 0 & .75 & 0 & 0 \\ 0 & 0 & 0 & .80 & 0 \\ 0 & 0 & 0 & 0 & 1.0 \end{bmatrix}.$$

Table 4.2. Depreciation policy

Class	Class life, years	Estimated salvage value,%	Depreciation method
Leasehold improvements	8	0	Straight line
Manufacturing equipment	6	20	Sum-of-the-years digits
Delivery trucks	5	25	Sum-of-the-years digits
Office furniture and fixtures	7	20	Straight line
Salesmen's autos	4	10	Double declining balance

You will note that since salvage values are not considered in determining the depreciation base under the double declining balance method (DDB), the entry in the B matrix for DDB items will always be 1.0. Proper allowance for salvage for such assets is handled as part of the R matrix. Using the information for class life and depreciation method, we can construct the matrix R as follows:

$$R = \begin{bmatrix} \frac{1}{8} & \frac{1}{8} & \frac{1}{8} & \frac{1}{8} & \frac{1}{8} & \frac{1}{8} & \frac{1}{8} & \frac{1}{8} \\ \frac{6}{21} & \frac{5}{21} & \frac{4}{21} & \frac{3}{21} & \frac{2}{21} & \frac{1}{21} & 0 & 0 \\ \frac{5}{15} & \frac{4}{15} & \frac{3}{15} & \frac{2}{15} & \frac{1}{15} & 0 & 0 & 0 \\ \frac{1}{7} & \frac{1}{7} & \frac{1}{7} & \frac{1}{7} & \frac{1}{7} & \frac{1}{7} & \frac{1}{7} & 0 \\ \frac{1}{2} & \frac{1}{4} & \frac{1}{8} & \frac{1}{40} & 0 & 0 & 0 & 0 \end{bmatrix}.$$

The first four rows of this matrix are self-explanatory. The entries in row five are calculated as follows:

For four-year-lived assets, the annual DDB depreciation rate is $2 \times \frac{1}{4} = \frac{1}{2}$.

Year 1. Depreciation $= \frac{1}{2}$ of cost.

Year 2. Depreciation $= \frac{1}{2}$ of remaining book value of $\frac{1}{2} = \frac{1}{4}$.

Year 3. Depreciation $= \frac{1}{2}$ of remaining book value of $\frac{1}{4} = \frac{1}{8}$.

Year 4. Depreciation $=$ amount required to reduce asset carrying amount to estimated salvage percentage of $10\% = \frac{1}{40}$.

Using this information, it is easy to show that the matrix product $C \cdot B \cdot R$ is a 1 × 8 row vector showing, for fixed-asset items purchased at time zero, the total depreciation expense for each year. If we want to array the expense for each year broken down by the five categories, we need only write down the individual component by component multiplications of $[C \cdot B]$ times R which make up the entries of the vector $C \cdot B \cdot R$. For the example at hand, if

$$C = \begin{bmatrix} 8,000 & 52,500 & 20,000 & 5,250 & 12,000 \end{bmatrix},$$

we have

$$C \cdot B = \begin{bmatrix} 8,000 & 52,5000 & 20,000 & 5,250 & 12,000 \end{bmatrix} \cdot \begin{bmatrix} 1.0 & 8 & 0 & 0 & 0 \\ 0 & .8 & 0 & 0 & 0 \\ 0 & 0 & .75 & 0 & 0 \\ 0 & 0 & 0 & .8 & 0 \\ 0 & 0 & 0 & 0 & 1.0 \end{bmatrix}$$

$$= \begin{bmatrix} 8,000 & 42,000 & 15,000 & 4,200 & 12,000 \end{bmatrix}.$$

Using this result, we can compute

$$C \cdot B \cdot R = \begin{bmatrix} 8,000 & 42,000 & 15,000 & 4,200 & 12,000 \end{bmatrix}$$

$$\cdot \begin{bmatrix} \frac{1}{8} & \frac{1}{8} & \frac{1}{8} & \frac{1}{8} & \frac{1}{8} & \frac{1}{8} & \frac{1}{8} & 0 \\ \frac{6}{21} & \frac{5}{21} & \frac{4}{21} & \frac{3}{21} & \frac{2}{21} & \frac{1}{21} & 0 & 0 \\ \frac{5}{15} & \frac{4}{15} & \frac{3}{15} & \frac{2}{15} & \frac{1}{15} & 0 & 0 & 0 \\ \frac{1}{7} & \frac{1}{7} & \frac{1}{7} & \frac{1}{7} & \frac{1}{7} & \frac{1}{7} & \frac{1}{7} & 0 \\ \frac{1}{2} & \frac{1}{4} & \frac{1}{8} & \frac{1}{10} & 0 & 0 & 0 & 0 \end{bmatrix}$$

$$= \begin{bmatrix} 24,600 & 18,600 & 14,100 & 9,900 & 6,600 & 3,600 & 1,600 & 1,000 \end{bmatrix}.$$

Then the desired lapse schedule is as shown in Table 4.3.

If such a schedule is prepared for the asset additions each year, the sum of such schedules, adjusted for retirements and trade-ins, will represent total depreciation expense for the company over the future life span of all fixed assets now in use.

We will now turn to the third major section of this chapter, a matrix approach to balance sheet valuation.

*4. MATRIX METHODS, MARKOV CHAINS, AND ACCOUNTING VALUATION

4.1 INTRODUCTION

As mentioned earlier, this last section of the chapter will present three problems in balance-sheet valuation which can be approached using matrix methods. All three deal with the issue of expected net realizable

---

*This section can be skipped without loss of continuity.

Table 4.3.

Years / Class	1	2	3	4	5	6	7	8	Totals
Leasehold improvements	1,000	1,000	1,000	1,000	1,000	1,000	1,000	1,000	8,000
Manufacturing equipment	12,000	10,000	8,000	6,000	4,000	2,000	0	0	42,000
Delivery trucks	5,000	4,000	3,000	2,000	1,000	0	0	0	15,000
Office furniture and fixtures	600	600	600	600	600	600	600	0	4,200
Salesmen's autos	6,000	3,000	1,500	300	0	0	0	0	10,800
Totals	24,600	18,600	14,100	9,900	6,600	3,600	1,600	1,000	80,000

value in a probabilistic context which draws heavily upon the matrix concepts we have been dealing with in preceding chapters. Before considering the valuation examples themselves, we will present an explanation of the probability model on which they are based, Markov chains, and a brief rationale for its use in approaching the valuation problem.

4.2 A MARKOV-CHAIN MODEL OF THE ACCOUNTS-RECEIVABLE PROCESS

As an illustration of Markov-chain ideas, consider the accounts-receivable collection process for a hypothetical department store. We will assume that every past charge-sales slip can be classified into one of the following five categories or stages:

1. Item is paid in full
2. Item is current (0–30 days old)
3. Item is past due (31–90 days old)
4. Item is being litigated (91–120 days old)
5. Item is deemed uncollectible (over 120 days old) and written off.

Further, we will assume that we only observe the status of outstanding charge slips at fixed, periodic intervals of one month. Over its life, each charge slip moves from category two (when it starts) through one or more of the other stages and finally winds up either in category one or category five. The path along which any one charge slip moves will be viewed here as a probabilistic variable. In other words, there are many different possible paths and the likelihood that any one path will be followed is calculable by formal mathematical procedures.

Since a charge slip moves through the collection process, as we have characterized it, in discrete steps, we need to be more precise in specifying the probabilistic nature of these moves or "transitions" before we can talk about actual probability calculations.

Let us assume that there is a number p_{ij} which represents the probability that an open sales slip now in stage i will switch to stage j in the next time period.* Since the elements p_{ij} are probabilities, we must have $0 \le p_{ij} \le 1$ for all i and j. Also, since an item cannot leave the

---

*More precisely, let D_n represent the stage an account is in at time n. Then $p_{ij} = \Pr(D_n = j/D_{n-1} = i)$. This is read, p_{ij} equals the probability that the account is in stage j at time n, given that it was in stage i at time $n-1$.

system as we have defined it, we must have $\Sigma_j \, p_{ij} = 1$. Let us further assume that switches in any time period depend only on the stage the item was in during the immediately preceding time period* (single-stage assumption), and that the transition probabilities do not themselves change over time† (stationarity assumption). If we define a stochastic process to be any sequence of events which follows probabilistic laws, the account-receivable aging process we have just described would be such a process. More precisely, it would be called a finite, absorbing, Markov-chain process with stationary transition probabilities. It is finite because it has a finite number of stages. It is a Markov process because it has the single-stage property. It is an absorbing process because it contains at least one absorbing stage or state. An absorbing stage is one which can be reached from other stages but which, once reached, can never be left. More precisely, state i is an absorbing stage just when $p_{ii} = 1$. In the example at hand, stages 1 and 5 are both absorbing. In considering a Markov chain such as this, it is customary to array transition probabilities in a form such as the following hypothetical matrix.

From \ To	1	5	2	3	4
1	1	0	0	0	0
5	0	1	0	0	0
2	.5	0	0	.5	0
3	.4	0	0	.4	.2
4	.5	.2	0	0	.3

A transition matrix arranged like this with the absorbing states listed first, followed by the nonabsorbing or "transient" states, is said to be in standard or "canonical" form. The importance of this arrangement stems from the fact that it facilitates the analysis of many interesting properties

---

*More precisely,

$$\Pr(D_n = j/D_1 = d_1, \ D_2 = d_2, \ \ldots, \ D_{n-1} = i) \ = \ \Pr(D_n = j/D_{n-1} = i).$$

Another way of stating this is to say that the future transitions an item may undergo are determined, probabilistically, by the stage at which it stands now and are not influenced at all by the transitions it went through to arrive at its current status.

† More precisely, $\Pr(D_n = j/D_{n-1} = i) = \Pr(D_m = j/D_{m-1} = i)$, for all m and n.

of a Markov process. For future reference, we will denote the subsections (partitions) of the canonical matrix in the following customary manner:

$$\left[\begin{array}{c|c} I & O \\ \hline R & Q \end{array} \right].$$

In this notation, since there are two absorbing stages and three transient ones, I is a 2×2 identity matrix, O is a 2×3 zero matrix, R is a matrix of dimension 3×2, and Q is a matrix of dimension 3×3.

4.3 USING THE MODEL

Although any formal representation such as this of a dynamic, interactive real-world process must be an oversimplification in many ways, this does not necessarily mean that it is not useful. If the representation or "model" captures the essence of the process with respect to the particular use for which it is intended, the fact that it does not capture all the subtleties of the overall process is not crucial. The question to ask in evaluating such a model, therefore, is not "Does it accurately reflect the overall process?", but rather, "Does it reflect the particular segment of the process in which we are interested accurately enough to be useful?"

We will be dealing here with the question of providing an adequate allowance for uncollectible accounts. Thus if the Markov-chain model deals adequately with the uncertainty of collection for outstanding charge slips, it need not consider or treat any other aspect of the credit-sales process. The model need not be a valid representation of any particular real-world situation. The literature dealing with actual applications does consider this problem, however. References (1), (3) and (5) at the end of the chapter are particularly helpful in this regard.

The problem of providing an adequate but not excessive allowance for uncollectible accounts is really one of measuring expected future write-offs against the current accounts-receivable balance. Viewing the allowance as an expectation suggests a probabilistic approach to measuring collections and write-offs. We are really interested, in other words, in the probability that any given account will go bad. If Markov chains can help us assess this probability, they are clearly relevant to this accounting valuation problem. Let us now illustrate specifically how they can be of use.

4.4. CONTRA-ASSET VALUATION: THE ALLOWANCE FOR DOUBTFUL ACCOUNTS*

In establishing an allowance for doubtful accounts for any firm with a high volume of charge-sale transactions of relatively small dollar-value, the common approach is to age the outstanding receivables and then multiply the total dollar amount in each age category by an estimated loss percentage. The sum of these expected loss values is the estimated allowance. This procedure is illustrated in Table 4.4. The only real problem in applying such a procedure is determining the appropriate loss percentages. The Markov-chain model presented in Section 4.2 provides a convenient way of computing the percentages directly. Thus if one accepts that model, computation of the allowance becomes a very straightforward process.

Table 4.4   Illustrative computation of allowance for doubtful accounts

Age category	Balance in accounts receivable at 12/31/1971	Estimated loss %	Estimated allowance required
0–30 days	$ 9,000.	.01	$ 90
31–90 days	$ 5,000.	.05	$250
91–120 days*	$ 2,000.	.10	$200
Totals	$16,000.		$540

*Anything over 120 days old is automatically written off as uncollectible.

Let a_{ij} be the probability that an open sales slip will eventually wind up in absorbing state j, given that it now stands in age category state i. Let A be the matrix with entries a_{ij}. Since the sales slip can either be absorbed in one transition or can switch to another transient state and be absorbed from there, we can express a_{ij} in terms of the following equation:

$$a_{ij} = r_{ij} + \sum_{k=1}^{3} q_{ik}a_{kj}.$$

In this notation, r_{ij} and q_{ik} represent entries in the corresponding partitions of the original transition matrix shown at the end of Section 4.2. Switching to matrix notation and remembering how matrix multiplication and

---

*The ideas presented in this section are adapted from the work by Cyert, Davidson, and Thompson cited as reference (3) at the end of the chapter.

addition are defined, we have

$$A = R + [Q \cdot A].$$

You can verify for yourself that all three of these matrices, A, R, and $[Q \cdot A]$, are of dimension 3×2 so that they do conform. Solving for A, we have

$$A - [Q \cdot A] = R,$$
$$[I - Q] \cdot A = R,$$
$$A = [I - Q]^{-1} \cdot R.$$

Thus A can be computed from information contained in the basic transition matrix. In the case at hand, A will have two columns corresponding to the two absorbing states and three rows corresponding to the three nonabsorbing ones. The column corresponding to stage 5, ultimate write-off, answers the question, "What is the probability that a charge slip now in a given age category will eventually become uncollectible?"

Let us further denote by B the 1×3 row vector representing the dollar balances in each of the three age categories at any point in time. Then the matrix product $B \cdot A$ is a 1×2 row vector whose entries represent, respectively, for the accounts-receivable balance, total expected dollars to be collected and total expected dollars to be written off. This latter amount is exactly what the allowance for uncollectible accounts is intended to reflect.

Let us now illustrate this procedure for the basic transition matrix and a hypothetical B vector of $[1,000,000 \quad 300,000 \quad 100,000]$. Step-by-step, the process is as follows:

1. Set up the matrix $[I - Q]$:

$$[I - Q] = \begin{bmatrix} 1 & 0 & 0 \\ 0 & 1 & 0 \\ 0 & 0 & 1 \end{bmatrix} - \begin{bmatrix} 0 & .5 & .0 \\ 0 & .4 & .2 \\ 0 & .0 & .3 \end{bmatrix} = \begin{bmatrix} 1 & -.5 & 0 \\ 0 & .6 & -.2 \\ 0 & 0 & .7 \end{bmatrix}.$$

2. Using row operations, compute the inverse matrix $[I - Q]^{-1}$:

$$[I - Q]^{-1} = \begin{bmatrix} 1 & -.5 & 0 \\ 0 & .6 & .2 \\ 0 & 0 & .7 \end{bmatrix}^{-1} - \cdots = \begin{bmatrix} 1 & .84 & .237 \\ 0 & 1.67 & .475 \\ 0 & 0 & 1.43 \end{bmatrix}.$$

3. Compute the A matrix:

$$A = [I - Q]^{-1} \cdot R = \begin{bmatrix} 1 & .84 & .237 \\ 0 & 1.67 & .475 \\ 0 & 0 & 1.43 \end{bmatrix} \cdot \begin{bmatrix} .5 & .0 \\ .4 & .0 \\ .5 & .2 \end{bmatrix} = \begin{bmatrix} .953 & .047 \\ .905 & .095 \\ .714 & .286 \end{bmatrix}.$$

4. Compute the matrix product $B \cdot A$:

$$B \cdot A = \begin{bmatrix} 1,000,000 & 300,000 & 100,000 \end{bmatrix} \cdot \begin{bmatrix} .953 & .047 \\ .905 & .095 \\ .714 & .286 \end{bmatrix}$$

$$= \begin{bmatrix} 1,295,900 & 104,100 \end{bmatrix}.$$

5. The second element of $B \cdot A$, \$104,100 , is the estimated allowance for uncollectible accounts.

Although this general approach represents an improvement over current practices only if the transition matrix is easier to estimate than the loss percentages themselves, this is often the case. Using very simply techniques explained in references (3) and (5), the transition probabilities can be estimated directly from observed transaction data. Since the loss percentages involve estimates of future events, they can never be directly measured under any circumstances. The Markov approach is thus manageable, computationally, if it is deemed to be useful, conceptually.

The essence of the doubtful-accounts problem we have just considered is to estimate the future net realizable flows from accounts receivable, allowing systematically for the uncertainty inherent in any such estimate. The Markov-chain model was found to be useful in estimating these flows. Since other balance-sheet valuations also require one to estimate expected realizable inflows or outflows, the Markov model should be more widely applicable than just to the area of accounts receivable. The next sections of this chapter will, in fact, present two additional areas in which it can be used.

4.5 ASSET VALUATION: THE NET REALIZABLE VALUE OF INVENTORY

Some accountants argue that the definition of an asset is something that will yield future inflows to the entity. From this definition, they conclude that assets should be measured in terms of their expected flows. Under this approach, inventory, as well as other assets, would be stated on the balance sheet at expected net realizable value. Although generally accepted accounting principles require the valuation of inventory at "cost" rather than net realizable value, there are still situations in conventional practice in which net realizable value is important information. In applying the "lower of cost or market" rule, for example, it is necessary to estimate net realizable value in establishing the upper and lower limits on market value. Also, merger or acquisition negotiations usually involve estimates of the "going-concern value" of existing assets. Many times in such circumstances, net realizable value is considered to be the best operational definition of going-concern value. Finally, internal management decisions relating to expanding or contracting an existing product line involve considerations of the net realizable value from investment in the inventory of the given line compared with alternative investment opportunities.

In short, there are many situations in which the net realizable value of inventory might be relevant information. In this section, we will present a variation of the Markov-chain model which can be used in some situations to estimate the net realizable value of inventories. The process has two stages. First is the projection of the expected physical flows of units through the manufacturing process, allowing for the probabilities of waste and scrap as well as ultimate sale. Second is the assignment of dollar amounts to these physical flows. We will consider the estimation of physical flows first.

Consider a hypothetical single-product firm which purchases raw material, converts it to finished product in a two-stage manufacturing process, and then ships the finished units under a long-term fixed-price contract. At each stage of production there is an inspection process which results in some units being scrapped and others being accepted. Raw material must also be inspected, and the price negotiated with the supplier is based on a "no-return" policy for substandard shipments. Backlogs often build up at the inspection stations. Units are thus not always able to move through the manufacturing process without delays. Assuming that all purchasing and production reporting is done on a monthly basis, the manufacturing process can be characterized as an absorbing Markov chain with a one-month transition period. We can thus represent it by the hypothetical transition matrix shown in Table 4.5.

We will further assume that all costs for the firm are variable and that cost data per unit are as follows.

Table 4.5.   Transition matrix

From \ To	Raw material 1	Semi-finished unit 2	Finished unit 3	Sold 4	Scrapped 5
1 Raw material	.5	.4	0	0	.1
2 Semifinished unit	0	.5	.35	0	.15
3 Finished unit	0	0	.1	.85	.05
4 Sold	0	0	0	1.0	0
5 Scrapped	0	0	0	0	1.0

Raw material cost	$10.00
Semifinishing cost	$ 5.00
Finishing cost	$25.00
Inspection cost (per inspection)	$ 4.00
Storage cost (per month)	$ 1.00
Scrap disposal cost	$ 7.00
Selling price	$85.00

At any point in time, the inventory is made up of units in each of the first three stages. Each of these units will eventually wind up in category 4 or 5. To move it through the manufacturing process, certain costs must be incurred. If the unit is eventually sold (category 4), revenue of $85.00 is realized. If it is scrapped (category 5), the firm must pay $7.00 to have it hauled away. Given the various possible paths, the possible outcomes, and the related payoffs, our problem is to measure the expected net realizable value of the inventory as a whole.

As an intermediate calculational step, we construct cost-flow matrix C (Table 4.6), which summarizes the dollar flows associated with each transition.

Table 4.6.   Cost-flow matrix C

From \ To	Raw material 1	Semi-finished unit 2	Finished unit 3	Sold 4	Scrapped 5
1 Raw material	1.00	10.00	0	0	11.00
2 Semifinished unit	0	1.00	30.00	0	11.00
3 Finished unit	0	0	1.00	(81.00)	11.00

An explanation of the entries in Table 4.6 is as follows:

Raw material to raw material	Storage	$ 1.00	$1.00
Raw material to semifinished	Processing	5.00	
	Inspection	4.00	
	Storage	1.00	10.00
Raw material to scrap	Inspection	4.00	
	Disposal	7.00	11.00
Semifinished to semifinished	Storage	1.00	1.00
Semifinished to finished	Processing	25.00	
	Inspection	4.00	
	Storage	1.00	30.00
Semifinished to scrap	Inspection	4.00	
	Disposal	7.00	11.00
Finished to finished	Storage	$ 1.00	$1.00
Finished to sold	Sales price	(85.00)	
	Inspection	4.00	(81.00)
Finished to scrap	Inspection	4.00	
	Disposal	7.00	11.00

To eliminate any possible confusion about algebraic signs in the following discussion, we will break the C matrix down into three partitions as follows:

$$\left[X_{3 \times 3} \mid Y_{3 \times 1} \mid Z_{3 \times 1} \right].$$

In this notation, X refers to the cash outflows for transient-to-transient transitions, Y refers to net cash inflows for absorptions into the revenue state, and Z refers to cash outflows for absorptions into the scrap state.

Combining the information in the transition matrix with the cash-flow matrix, we can write the following expression for the net realizable value v_i of a unit now in stage i:

$$v_i = r_{i4}y_{i4} - r_{i5}z_{i5} + \sum_{j=1}^{3} q_{ij}(v_j - x_{ij}). \tag{1}$$

Although this looks formidable at first glance, it is really not very complex when the individual parts are analyzed. First, the r and q elements refer, respectively, to the transient-to-absorbing and transient-to-transient partitions of the transition matrix. The first product term, $r_{i4} \cdot y_{i4}$, represents the contribution to expected value due to sale in the next period. The following term, $r_{i5} z_{i5}$, represents the expected cost due to scrapping in the next period. The summation term, $\Sigma_{j=1}^{3} q_{ij}(v_j - x_{ij})$, represents the contribution to expected value for a unit which switches to another transient state, j, in the next period, allowing for the costs incurred in making that transition.

If we denote $r_{i4}y_{i4}$ by $\bar{y}_i$, $r_{i5}z_{i5}$ by $\bar{z}_i$, and $\Sigma_{j=1}^{3} q_{ij}x_{ij}$ by $\bar{x}_i$, Eq. (1) becomes

$$v_i = \bar{y}_i - \bar{z}_i + \Sigma_{j=1}^{3} q_{ij}v_j - \bar{x}_i.$$

Letting $h_i = [\bar{y}_i - \bar{z}_i - \bar{x}_i]$ and switching to matrix notation, we have

$$V = H + QV.$$

This step should be clear if you remember that the formula for the ith term of the product matrix QV is given by $\Sigma_{j=1}^{3} q_{ij}v_j$. The procedure in solving for the vector V should now also be clear. Specifically, we have

$$V - QV = H,$$
$$[I-Q]V = H,$$
$$V = [I-Q]^{-1}H.$$

Using the hypothetical numbers above, we can illustrate this procedure as follows:

1. $X = \begin{bmatrix} 1.00 & 10.00 & 0 \\ 0 & 1.00 & 30.00 \\ 0 & 0 & 1.00 \end{bmatrix}$, $Y = \begin{bmatrix} 0 \\ 0 \\ 81.00 \end{bmatrix}$, $Z = \begin{bmatrix} 11.00 \\ 11.00 \\ 11.00 \end{bmatrix}$.

2. $Q = \begin{bmatrix} .5 & .4 & 0 \\ 0 & .5 & .35 \\ 0 & 0 & .1 \end{bmatrix}$, $R = \begin{bmatrix} 0 & .1 \\ 0 & .15 \\ .85 & .05 \end{bmatrix}$.

3. $\bar{X} = \begin{bmatrix} .5(1) + .4(10) + 0 \\ 0 + .5(1) + .35(30) \\ 0 + 0 + .1(1) \end{bmatrix} = \begin{bmatrix} 4.50 \\ 11.00 \\ .10 \end{bmatrix}$,

$$\overline{Y} = \begin{bmatrix} 0 \\ 0 \\ .85(81) \end{bmatrix} = \begin{bmatrix} 0 \\ 0 \\ 68.85 \end{bmatrix},$$

$$\overline{Z} = \begin{bmatrix} .1(11) \\ .15(11) \\ .05(11) \end{bmatrix} = \begin{bmatrix} 1.10 \\ 1.65 \\ .55 \end{bmatrix}.$$

4. $$H = \overline{Y} - \overline{Z} - \overline{X} = \begin{bmatrix} 0 \\ 0 \\ 68.85 \end{bmatrix} - \begin{bmatrix} 1.10 \\ 1.65 \\ .55 \end{bmatrix} - \begin{bmatrix} 4.50 \\ 11.00 \\ .10 \end{bmatrix} = \begin{bmatrix} -5.60 \\ -12.65 \\ 68.20 \end{bmatrix}.$$

5. $$[I-Q] = \begin{bmatrix} 1 & 0 & 0 \\ 0 & 1 & 0 \\ 0 & 0 & 1 \end{bmatrix} - \begin{bmatrix} .5 & .4 & 0 \\ 0 & .5 & .35 \\ 0 & 0 & .1 \end{bmatrix} = \begin{bmatrix} .5 & -.4 & 0 \\ 0 & .5 & -.35 \\ 0 & 0 & .9 \end{bmatrix}.$$

6. $$V = [I-Q]^{-1}H = \begin{bmatrix} 2 & 1.6 & .62 \\ 0 & 2 & .78 \\ 0 & 0 & 1.1 \end{bmatrix} \cdot \begin{bmatrix} -5.60 \\ -12.65 \\ 68.20 \end{bmatrix} = \begin{bmatrix} 9.84 \\ 27.90 \\ 75.02 \end{bmatrix}.$$

This vector represents the expected realizable value for units which are now in the raw-material, semifinished, and finished stages, respectively. If the number of units in each of the three processing stages at a point in time is represented by the three-component row vector B, the matrix product BV is the desired estimate of net realizable value for the inventory as a whole. Assuming $B = \begin{bmatrix} 10{,}000 & 30{,}000 & 5{,}000 \end{bmatrix}$, we have

$$BV = \begin{bmatrix} 10{,}000 & 30{,}000 & 5{,}000 \end{bmatrix} \cdot \begin{bmatrix} 9.84 \\ 27.90 \\ 75.02 \end{bmatrix} = \$1{,}310{,}500.$$

The illustration we have just presented dealt only with the uncertainty of physical unit flows, treating the related dollar values as known. This was done in order not to unnecessarily complicate an introductory example. The model itself, however, is flexible enough to be useful in situations where the uncertainty of dollar values is more important that that of physical flows or where both kinds of uncertainty must be dealt with formally. A more realistic example which also considers nonvariable costs more fully is presented in reference (5) at the end of this chapter. In general, this approach to measuring expected net realizable value of inventories could be useful in any situation which can be characterized in terms of discrete production stages and regular, recurring product flow patterns. Whether the approach is useful in any specific situation is an empirical question which can be answered using statistical techniques which are also explained in reference (5).

We will now turn to the third valuation example based on a Markov-chain model.

4.6 LIABILITY VALUATION: THE ESTIMATED WARRANTY LIABILITY

In order to illustrate the broad potential applicability of the kind of Markov model we have been considering, we will now present an example from the right side of the balance sheet to complement the two previous ones, which dealt with the left side.

Whenever a warranty is provided on a company's products, the accountant is faced with the problem of estimating the future costs under warranty in order to fairly present total liabilities for balance-sheet purposes. Although the amount is uncertain, the contractual liability is definite. An estimate of warranty expense must therefore be made in order to achieve a proper matching of revenue and expense in the current period when the sale is recorded. This measurement problem is another example of estimating expected future flows. The fact that they are outflows this time instead of net inflows doesn't change the nature of the problem. If the situation can be characterized as a Markov process, therefore, a procedure similar to the one already considered could be used to estimate the liability.

Let us assume that the Acme Products Company extends a two-year warranty on parts and labor for its electric can opener, which is marketed nationally through department stores and discount chains. If the product proves defective within the two-year period, the customer can return it to Acme to be repaired at Acme's expense. Once a unit has been repaired, the warranty is no longer in effect. Acme considers this policy to be fair to the customer because virtually all warranty complaints result from the quality-control problems of a mass-production operation. Once a unit has been reworked by hand by a repairman, there is no significant chance of its failing again within two years.

Past history also shows that virtually all complaints result from failure in one or another of four critical parts which are particularly sensitive to the variations in the assembly operation. Since all four parts together account for only $1.50 of the cost of the unit, which retails for $19.95, Acme has found it cheaper to just replace all four of them on all service calls rather than spend time testing them. A service job thus normally consists of $\frac{1}{2}$ hour of a repairman's time and the four replacement parts. In nearly all cases, the unit is then ready to be returned to the customer. In short, although there is a small chance of a greater amount, a repair order on the electric can opener usually costs Acme $4.50, counting material and labor. The troublesome issue is estimating how many units will be returned, not what the repair cost will be on the returned units.

At any point in time, the "inventory" of units under warranty can be thought of in discrete annual stages. We can represent this "inventory" by a two-component row vector B. The first component, b_1, represents units from 0–1 year old and still under warranty. Similarly, the second component, b_2, represents units from 1 to 2 years old and still under warranty.

Making use of the statistical sampling techniques referred to earlier, Acme had been able to develop the following estimates:

Probability that a unit will become defective in its first year of service $-$ .2.

Probability that a unit which did not become defective in the first year of service will do so in the second year $=$ .1.

Thinking of the process in these terms and assuming that "expiration of the warranty" and "unit requires servicing" are both absorbing states, we can construct the matrix shown in Table 4.7.

From here, the procedure for estimating total units which will require servicing is identical to the procedure outlined earlier for estimating the dollar volume of accounts receivable which will not be collected. Specifically, we first compute the matrix A whose i,jth entry, a_{ij}, represents the probability that a unit now in transient state i will ultimately be absorbed into absorbing state j. This matrix is calculated from the formula $A = [I - Q]^{-1} \cdot R$, where Q and R refer, respectively, to the "transient-to-transient" and "transient-to-absorbing" partitions of the transition matrix. Then, for a given "inventory" vector B of units outstanding under warranty, we form the matrix product $B \cdot A$. This product is a two-

Table 4.7.

From \ To	0-1 yr. old and still under warranty 1	1–2 yrs. old and still under warranty 2	Expiration of the warranty 3	Unit requires servicing 4
1 0–1 yr. old and still under warranty	0	.8	0	.2
2 1–2 yrs. old and still under warranty	0	0	.9	.1
3 Expiration of the warranty	0	0	1	0
4 Unit requires servicing	0	0	0	1

component row vector, the second element of which represents the expected number of units now outstanding under warranty which will eventually require servicing. This quantity, multiplied by $4.50 per unit, is the desired "estimated warranty liability."

For Acme Products, if $B = [400,000 \ 300,000]$, the process can be summarized as follows.

1. $Q = \begin{bmatrix} 0 & .8 \\ 0 & 0 \end{bmatrix}, \quad R = \begin{bmatrix} 0 & .2 \\ .9 & .1 \end{bmatrix}.$

2. $[I-Q] = \begin{bmatrix} 1 & 0 \\ 0 & 1 \end{bmatrix} - \begin{bmatrix} 0 & .8 \\ 0 & 0 \end{bmatrix} = \begin{bmatrix} 1 & -.8 \\ 0 & 1 \end{bmatrix}.$

3. $[I-Q]^{-1} = \begin{bmatrix} 1 & -.8 \\ 0 & 1 \end{bmatrix}^{-1} = \ldots = \begin{bmatrix} 1 & .8 \\ 0 & 1 \end{bmatrix}.$

4. $A = I - Q^{-1} \cdot R = \begin{bmatrix} 1 & .8 \\ 0 & 1 \end{bmatrix} \cdot \begin{bmatrix} 0 & .2 \\ .9 & .1 \end{bmatrix} = \begin{bmatrix} .72 & .28 \\ .9 & .1 \end{bmatrix}.$

5. $B \cdot A = [400,000 \quad 300,000] \cdot \begin{bmatrix} .72 & .28 \\ .9 & .1 \end{bmatrix} = [558,000 \quad 142,000].$

6.   Estimated warranty liability $= (\$4.50) \cdot (142,000) = \$639,000.$

4.7 SUMMARY

The purpose of the last three sections is not to suggest that all or even most balance-sheet valuation problems can be approached in a matrix context using Markov models. There are probably situations in which such an approach could be helpful, but the intent here is only to illustrate, not to prescribe. Many accountants feel that the development of a "theory of valuation" in accounting has often been held back by the related measurement problems. It is true in many disciplines that theory development and measurement skill go hand in hand. New measurement techniques make possible the extension of earlier theory, and new theory, in turn, suggests desired innovations in measurement. This set of examples applying matrix methods to accounting measurement problems is offered in the hope that they might contribute to the continuing interdependent development of theory and measurement techniques with regard to the valuation question in accounting.

4.8 A REFINEMENT OF THE VALUATION MODELS TO REFLECT DISCOUNTING

Since all three of the Markov valuation models considered in this chapter involve an expected sum of future flows which will be realized over a period of years, one can argue that discounting of the flows is necessary. Clearly, a cash receipt to be received four years hence has less current significance than one to be received tomorrow, because of the "time-value" of money. A sum of money to be received now can be invested at interest and thus has more "present value" than an identical sum of money to be received at some point in the future. Specifically, it can be shown that if the "value of money" is $d\%$, a sum money A to be received in n years is only worth $A/(1 + d)^n$ today. Thus in order to fairly reflect the value of a series of cash flows to be realized over a period of years, each flow should be expressed in terms of its so-called "present value." If the flow in the ith year is c_i, for example, its present value is only $c_i/(1 + d)^i$, and the present value of the series is $\Sigma_i c_i/(1 + d)^i$.

There is much controversy among accountants as to whether discounting is appropriate in balance-sheet valuations, because such valuations are not usually based on expected future flows. There is also much controversy about what the discounting rate should represent, even among those who feel that discounting is desirable. Involvement in either of these arguments is really beyond the scope of this book. The purpose of this section is merely to illustrate that discounting can be easily incorporated into any of the models presented, if it is deemed appropriate and if a discount rate is given. A rate of 10 percent will be used here for illustrative purposes.

If d is the discount rate, a related measure is the "discount factor" D which is defined to be $1/1 + d$. The discount factor is a more convenient notational form than the discount rate. For example, instead of writing the present value of the ith flow as $c_i/(1 + d)^i$ as we did earlier, we can more compactly write $D^i c_i$. We will adopt this shortened form in the discussion which follows. Since $d = 10$ percent, we have $D = 1/(1 + .1)$, or $.909$.

In the accounts receivable example, supposing that B is the vector of beginning dollar balances, we will show that the present value of future collections and write-offs is given by $B[I - DQ]^{-1} \cdot R$, where Q and R are as before and D is the discount factor. This is a very simple extension of the earlier result which did not consider discounting. You will remember that it showed collections and write-offs to be equal to $B[I - Q]^{-1} \cdot R$.

To derive this result, we first will introduce a period-by-period approach to looking at expected collections and write-offs. Remembering the definitions of B and R, we would expect collections and write-offs in the current period to be $B \cdot R$. Expected dollars to be absorbed one period hence can be expressed as BQR, since QR represents the probabilities of not being absorbed in this period and then being absorbed one period hence. The present value of the amounts to be realized one period hence is $B[DQR]$, where D is the discount factor. Similarly, expected dollars to be absorbed two periods hence can be expressed as $[B \cdot Q^2 \cdot R]$. The present value of this amount is $[BD^2Q^2R]$. In general, expected absorptions in the kth period are $[BQ^kR]$ with present value of $B[D^kQ^kR]$. The total present value of expected collections and write-offs over all future periods, therefore, can be written as the sum

$$BR + BDQR + BD^2Q^2R + \cdots + BD^kQ^kR + \cdots$$

Using a little sleight-of-hand, we can make the following switch:

$$\begin{aligned} & BR + BDQR + BD^2Q^2R + \cdots + BD^kQ^kR + \cdots \\ & = B[I + DQ + D^2Q^2 + \cdots + D^kQ^k + \cdots]R. \end{aligned} \tag{1}$$

Once you have digested this move, hold your hat because the next one represents a brilliant bit of mathematic insight on the part of some long-since-forgotten mathematician. Notice what happens when we multiply the matrix quantity $[I + DQ + D^2Q^2 + \cdots + D^kQ^k + \cdots]$ by the matrix quantity $[I - DQ]$:

$$[I + DQ + D^2Q^2 + \cdots + D^kQ^k + \cdots] \cdot [I - DQ]$$
$$= I + DQ + D^2Q^2 + \cdots + D^kQ^k + \cdots - DQ - D^2Q^2 - \cdots - D^kQ^k - \cdots$$
$$= I.$$

In other words, although it is by no means obvious at first glance, we have

$$[I - DQ] \cdot [I + DQ + D^2Q^2 + \cdots D^kQ^k + \cdots] = I.$$

You will remember that the definition of the inverse of a matrix A is the matrix which, when multiplied times A, yields an identity matrix. We can thus write

$$I + DQ + D^2Q^2 + \cdots + D^kQ^k + \cdots = [I - DQ]^{-1}.$$

Making this substitution in equation (1) above produces the stated result. Specifically,

$$BR + BDQR + BD^2Q^2R + \cdots + BD^kQ^kR + \cdots$$
$$= B[I + DQ + D^2Q^2 + \cdots + D^kQ^k + \cdots]R \qquad (2)$$
$$= B[I - DQ]^{-1}R.$$

Equation (1) is impossible to deal with, calculationally, because it includes an unending ("infinite") sequence of terms. The alternative form shown in equation (2), however, is very manageable. The matrix $[I - DQ]^{-1}$ is no more difficult to compute than its undiscounted equivalent $[I - Q]^{-1}$. We can illustrate the discounting procedure using the same example we considered earlier. Specifically, we have the following:

1.
$$Q = \begin{bmatrix} 0 & .5 & 0 \\ 0 & .4 & .2 \\ 0 & 0 & .3 \end{bmatrix}, \quad R = \begin{bmatrix} .5 & 0 \\ .4 & 0 \\ .5 & .2 \end{bmatrix}.$$

2.
$$DQ = .909\, Q = .909 \begin{bmatrix} 0 & .5 & 0 \\ 0 & .4 & .2 \\ 0 & 0 & .3 \end{bmatrix} = \begin{bmatrix} 0 & .455 & 0 \\ 0 & .364 & .182 \\ 0 & 0 & .273 \end{bmatrix}.$$

3.
$$[I - DQ] = \begin{bmatrix} 1 & 0 & 0 & 0 \\ 0 & 1 & 0 & -0 \\ 0 & 0 & 1 & 0 \end{bmatrix} \begin{bmatrix} .455 & & 0 \\ .364 & .182 \\ 0 & .273 \end{bmatrix} = \begin{bmatrix} 1 & -.455 & & 0 \\ 0 & .634 & -.182 \\ 0 & 0 & .727 \end{bmatrix}.$$

4.
$$[I - DQ]^{-1} = \begin{bmatrix} 1 & -.455 & 0 \\ 0 & .634 & -.182 \\ 0 & 0 & .727 \end{bmatrix}^{-1} = \cdots = \begin{bmatrix} 1 & .72 & .18 \\ 0 & 1.58 & .40 \\ 0 & 0 & 1.38 \end{bmatrix}.$$

5. $B = [1,000,000 \quad 3,000,000 \quad 100,000].$

6. $B\,[I - DQ]^{-1} \cdot R$

$$= [1,000,000 \quad 300,000 \quad 100,000] . \begin{bmatrix} 1 & .72 & .18 \\ 0 & 1.58 & .40 \\ 0 & 0 & 1.38 \end{bmatrix} \begin{bmatrix} .5 & 0 \\ .4 & 0 \\ .5 & .2 \end{bmatrix}$$

$$= [1,196,600 \quad 87,600].$$

Remembering that the only change in the accounts-receivable example to incorporate discounting was the substitution of the matrix $[I - DQ]^{-1}$ for $[I - Q]^{-1}$, where D is the discount factor, one might expect a parallel result for the inventory-valuation example. Such a result would show the discounted present value of V to be equal to $[I - DQ]^{-1}H$. The use of such a result, however, should not be based solely on an argument by analogy. As we shall soon see, its validity can be demonstrated analytically in this second situation as well. The undiscounted expression for the net realizable value of a unit now in transient state i, v_i, was given by

$$v_i = h_i + \Sigma_j q_{ij} v_j. \tag{3}$$

The flows represented by h_i are all next-period flows which do not require discounting. Thus the only change we must make in the equation to allow for discounting is to acknowledge that the one-period-hence values, v_j, have a present value of only Dv_j. Incorporating this change, we have

$$v_i = h_i + \Sigma_j q_{ij} (Dv_j). \tag{4}$$

Since D is a constant (scalar), it can be factored outside the summation to produce the following result:

$$v_i = h_i + D\Sigma_j q_{ij} v_j. \tag{5}$$

Switching to matrix notation, we have

$$V = H + DQV. \tag{6}$$

Solving for V, we obtain

$$V - DQV = H,$$
$$[I - DQ]V = H,$$
$$V = [I - DQ]^{-1} \cdot H.$$

This is the desired result, which we can easily substitute in the matrix product $B \cdot V$ to yield a present-value measure of the expected net realizable value of the inventory at any point in time.

For the same example we used earlier, we have

1. $Q = \begin{bmatrix} .5 & .4 & 0 \\ 0 & .5 & .35 \\ 0 & 0 & .1 \end{bmatrix}, \qquad H = \begin{bmatrix} -5.60 \\ -12.65 \\ 68.20 \end{bmatrix}.$

2. $DQ = .909 \begin{bmatrix} .5 & .4 & 0 \\ 0 & .5 & .35 \\ 0 & 0 & .1 \end{bmatrix} = \begin{bmatrix} .455 & .364 & 0 \\ 0 & .455 & .318 \\ 0 & 0 & .091 \end{bmatrix}.$

3. $[I - DQ] = \begin{bmatrix} 1 & 0 & 0 \\ 0 & 1 & 0 \\ 0 & 0 & 1 \end{bmatrix} - \begin{bmatrix} .455 & .364 & 0 \\ 0 & .455 & .318 \\ 0 & 0 & .091 \end{bmatrix} = \begin{bmatrix} .455 & -.364 & 0 \\ 0 & .455 & -.318 \\ 0 & 0 & .909 \end{bmatrix}.$

4. $[I - DQ]^{-1} = \begin{bmatrix} .455 & -.364 & 0 \\ 0 & .455 & -.318 \\ 0 & 0 & .909 \end{bmatrix}^{-1} = \cdots = \begin{bmatrix} 1.835 & 1.228 & .430 \\ 0 & 1.835 & .642 \\ 0 & 0 & 1.100 \end{bmatrix}.$

5. $V = [I - DQ]^{-1} \cdot H = \begin{bmatrix} 1.835 & 1.228 & .430 \\ 0 & 1.835 & .642 \\ 0 & 0 & 1.100 \end{bmatrix} \cdot \begin{bmatrix} -5.60 \\ -12.65 \\ 68.20 \end{bmatrix} = \begin{bmatrix} 3.49 \\ 20.53 \\ 75.02 \end{bmatrix}.$

6. $B = [10,000 \quad 30,000 \quad 5,000].$

7. $B \cdot V = [10,000 \quad 30,000 \quad 5,000] \cdot \begin{bmatrix} 3.49 \\ 20.53 \\ 75.02 \end{bmatrix} = 1,025,900.$

The derivation of the parallel result for the warranty-liability example follows the same general line of reasoning as the two preceding examples.

We first define a two-component column vector W, the elements of which, w_i, represent expected warranty cost for a unit now in transient state i. Using the same logic as in Eq. (1) in Section 4.5 and ignoring discounting for the moment, we can write

$$w_i = r_{i2}c + \sum_{i=1}^{2} q_{ij}w_j.$$

where c is the cost of repairing a unit under warranty, or \$4.50. This equation simply says that expected warranty cost for a unit now in state i is the sum of two factors. The first is the probability of the unit's becoming defective next period multiplied by the resulting warranty cost. This is the factor $r_{i2}c$. The second factor is the sum of the probabilities of all the units' moving to another transient state j next period, each multiplied by the expected warranty cost associated with that state. This is the factor

$$\sum_{i=1}^{2} q_{ij}w_j.$$

To allow for discounting, we do not need to change the factor $r_{i2}c$, since this represents next-period flows. We need only recognize the fact that the one-period-hence quantities, w_j, in the second factor have present value of only Dw_j. Thus an expression incorporating discounting is as follows:

$$w_i = r_{i2}c + \sum_{i=1}^{2} q_{ij}Dw_j.$$

Let $r_{i2}c = x_i$. X is thus a two-component column vector made up of the elements in the second column of R each multiplied by c, which in our example is \$4.50. Following the same logic as that used in going from Eq. (4) to Eq. (6) in the present section, we can write

$$W = X + DQW.$$

It should be clear to you that we can then write

$$W = [I - DQ]^{-1} \cdot X.$$

For the numbers used in the earlier example, you should be able to satisfy yourself that

$$W = [I - DQ]^{-1} \cdot X = \cdots = \begin{bmatrix} 1.23 \\ .45 \end{bmatrix}.$$

The desired estimate for the present value of the warranty liability is given by $B \cdot W$. If $B = [400{,}000 \quad 300{,}000]$ we have

$$B \cdot W = [400{,}000 \quad 300{,}000] \cdot \begin{bmatrix} 1.23 \\ .45 \end{bmatrix} = \$627{,}000.$$

SELECTED REFERENCES

1. Anderson, T. W., and L. A. Goodman. "Statistical Inference about Markov Chains," *Annals of Mathematical Statistics*, Vol. 28, 1957, pp. 89–110.
2. Corcoran, A. Wayne. *Mathematical Applications in Accounting*. Harcourt, Brace & World, New York, 1968. Especially Chapter 7.
3. Cyert, R. M., H. J. Davidson, and G. L. Thompson. "Estimation of the Allowance for Doubtful Accounts by Markov Chains," *Management Science*, April 1962.
4. Kemeny, John, Arthur Schleifer, J. Laurie Snell, and Gerald Thompson. *Finite Mathematics with Business Applications*. Prentice-Hall, Englewood Cliffs, N.J. 1962. Especially Chapters 4 and 5.
5. Shank, John. "Income Determination under Uncertainty: An Application of of Markov Chains," *The Accounting Review*, January 1971.

Chapter Five

MATRIX METHODS
IN FINANCIAL PLANNING

1. INTRODUCTION

In this chapter we consider three examples of the ways matrix methods can help to solve problems related to financial planning. Two of the examples are based on the Markov-chain models discussed in Chapter 4. The other example is based on the concept of input-output analysis. This concept was originally viewed as a way of dealing systematically with aggregate supply and demand interrelationships in our national economy. Many people, however, have also applied the idea to planning problems at the level of an individual firm.

References (2), (5), (6), and (7) at the end of this chapter represent some examples of input-output analysis applied at this micro level. There is still much controversy as to whether the ideas can really be transferred out of the macro context. Reference (4) is a good summary of this controversy. Since the purpose of this book is to consider the *potential* applicability of matrix methods in accounting, we won't try to evaluate the controversy here. The reader should be aware, however, that there are differences of opinion as to how useful the ideas we will discuss really are. It is such controversies that provide much of the excitement and intellectual challenge that characterize accounting today.

2. INPUT-OUTPUT ANALYSIS: A TWO-PRODUCT PLANNING MODEL

2.1 THE MODEL

Consider a firm which has two departments, each producing a single product and each using only one production method. Each department uses a part of the other's output as an input in its own production process. Further, assume that the production function in each department is "linear with constant coefficients." In general, if Y is the level of output and if the various production inputs are denoted by x_i, a "linear" production function is one with the following form:

$$Y = \sum_{i=1}^{n} a_i x_i = a_1 x_1 + a_2 x_2 + \cdots + a_n x_n.$$

If the coefficients a_i don't change over time, we say that the production function has "constant coefficients." Since one of the production inputs is overhead expense, the linearity condition implies that all overhead is purely variable. This requirement can be relaxed in more complicated examples, but we will not build in such a refinement here. Finally, we assume that the prices of all inputs and outputs are known and the interdepartmental transfers are valued at selling prices.

We represent the input-output relationships for the firm as a matrix M which has four main partitions as follows:

$$M_{6 \times 3} = \left[\begin{array}{c|c} A_{2 \times 2} & B_{2 \times 1} \\ \hline C_{4 \times 2} & D_{4 \times 1} \end{array} \right].$$

The rows of M represent inputs and the columns outputs. The partition A represents interdepartmental transfers. B is a two-component column vector representing total external demand for the two products. This demand can be the result of sales or planned inventory accumulation. The partition C represents the usage of production inputs, other than the two end-products themselves, in the production process of each department. In this example, we will consider such inputs to be raw material, labor, overhead, and profits. Profits are included as an input because the matrix formulation of the production process requires that the value of output (row totals) be equal to the sum of the values of the inputs (column totals). Completing the description of the partitions, D is a four-component zero column vector.

Table 5.1.   Input-output matrix

Outputs / Inputs	Product I	Product II	Sales and inventory	Total output
Product I	0	25	100	125
Product II	40	0	200	240
Raw material	30	100	0	
Labor	25	60	0	
Overhead	20	30	0	
Profits	10	25	0	
Total inputs	125	240		

We illustrate this matrix formulation with a hypothetical example. We assume that the input-output matrix was constructed from cost-accounting records covering some prior period which management considers to be representative of the production process (Table 5.1).

For this matrix, we have

$$A = \begin{bmatrix} 0 & 25 \\ 40 & 0 \end{bmatrix}.$$

$$B = \begin{bmatrix} 100 \\ 200 \end{bmatrix}.$$

$$C = \begin{bmatrix} 30 & 100 \\ 25 & 60 \\ 20 & 30 \\ 10 & 25 \end{bmatrix}.$$

$$D = \begin{bmatrix} 0 \\ 0 \\ 0 \\ 0 \end{bmatrix}.$$

Assuming that the proportions of each input used in producing a unit of output are fixed, we can compute a set of "input-output coefficients" for each product by simply expressing each element of A and C as a percentage of the appropriate column total. The set of such coefficients can be expressed as two new matrices. We will denote these coefficient matrices by E and F, where E refers to the interdepartmental inputs and F to the other inputs. For the example at hand, we have

$$E = \begin{bmatrix} 0 & \frac{25}{240} \\ \frac{40}{125} & 0 \end{bmatrix} = \begin{bmatrix} 0 & .014 \\ .320 & 0 \end{bmatrix}.$$

$$F = \begin{bmatrix} \frac{30}{125} & \frac{100}{240} \\ \frac{25}{125} & \frac{60}{240} \\ \frac{20}{125} & \frac{30}{240} \\ \frac{10}{125} & \frac{25}{240} \end{bmatrix} = \begin{bmatrix} .240 & .417 \\ .200 & .250 \\ .160 & .125 \\ .080 & .104 \end{bmatrix}.$$

2.2 USING THE MODEL

By this time, your are probably asking yourself why we have gone to so much trouble to generate these coefficient matrices E and F. The question is certainly a legitimate one, but it is also easily answered. As we shall soon see, we can use E and F to estimate the level of output necessary in each department to support any projected goal for sales and inventory accumulation and to prepare a departmental production plan or budget based on such a goal. Input-output analysis is thus very useful in developing integrated financial plans based on overall output goals.

Let us assume, for example, that the projected sales and inventory target for next year is as follows:

	Projected sales	Desired inventory accumulation	Total
Product I	$100	$100	$200
Product II	$200	$100	$300

With these figures, the projected vector B, described above, becomes

$$B = \begin{bmatrix} 200 \\ 300 \end{bmatrix}.$$

If we denote by X the vector of departmental output totals necessary to support this level of external demand, we can write the following equation:

$$X = [E \cdot X] + B.$$

This states that X must be large enough to allow for interdepartmental usage, as summarized in E, as well as for external requirements.

You should be very familiar by this time with the procedure for solving a matrix equation of the form $X = EX + B$, when E and B are known. Specifically, we have

$$X = EX + B,$$
$$X - EX = B,$$
$$[I - E] X = B,$$
$$X = [I - E]^{-1} \cdot B.$$

For the example at hand, the procedure is as follows:

1. $E = \begin{bmatrix} 0 & .104 \\ .320 & 0 \end{bmatrix}.$

2. $[I - E] = \begin{bmatrix} 1 & 0 \\ 0 & 1 \end{bmatrix} - \begin{bmatrix} 0 & .104 \\ .320 & 0 \end{bmatrix} = \begin{bmatrix} 1 & -.104 \\ -.320 & 1 \end{bmatrix}.$

3. By using row operations, we obtain

$$[I - E]^{-1} = \begin{bmatrix} 1 & -.104 \\ -.320 & 1 \end{bmatrix}^{-1} = \cdots = \begin{bmatrix} 1.034 & .107 \\ .331 & 1.034 \end{bmatrix}.$$

4. $X = [I - E]^{-1} \cdot B = \begin{bmatrix} 1.034 & .107 \\ .331 & 1.034 \end{bmatrix} \cdot \begin{bmatrix} 200 \\ 300 \end{bmatrix} = \begin{bmatrix} 238.9 \\ 376.4 \end{bmatrix}.$

Thus we must produce $238.9 worth of product I and $376.4 worth of product II in order to meet the desired external demand target.

If we denote by Y the vector of input requirements, other than the end-products themselves, necessary to support a level of output equal to X, we can write the following equation for Y:

$$Y = F \cdot X.$$

This expression should be clear if you remember how we defined the coefficient matrix F. For the example at hand, we have

$$Y = F \cdot X = \begin{bmatrix} .240 & .417 \\ .200 & .250 \\ .160 & .125 \\ .080 & .104 \end{bmatrix} \cdot \begin{bmatrix} 238.9 \\ 376.4 \end{bmatrix} = \begin{bmatrix} 214.5 \\ 141.9 \\ 85.8 \\ 58.3 \end{bmatrix}.$$

In words, we can interpret this result as follows:

$$\begin{aligned}
\text{Raw material usage} &= \$214.5 \\
\text{Labor usage} &= \$141.9 \\
\text{Overhead usage} &= \$\ 85.8 \\
\text{Profit} &= \$\ 58.3
\end{aligned}$$

There are several ways we can use the information in the vector Y in the context of financial planning decisions. If we can express plant capacity with respect to any input in dollar terms, we can measure the extent of capacity utilization implied by the given production plan. If utilization seems unduly low, we might consider cutting back our capacity, if possible, as a cost-saving step. We might also explore ways of increasing the production target to better utilize the available quantity of that input. If expected usage exceeds capacity, we must either adjust the target downward or make arrangements to increase our capacity. Considerations like these might be particularly relevant with regard to an input such as labor which can often be expanded or contracted as desired, if enough lead-time is allowed.

In addition to its use in evaluating over- and under-capacity problems, the vector Y can also be used in projecting the cash-flow requirements of the production plan. Knowing, for example, that $214.5 of outside raw-material purchases will be needed enables us to consider in advance the best way to finance the purchases, considering the sources of funds available to the firm and the other uses for them. Further, relating the level of purchases required to the firm's inventory policies may highlight potential problems in warehouse capacity, in the manning of the receiving department, or in the workload of the purchasing department.

We should mention that the profit component of $58.3 in Y does not correspond to the profit which will appear on the income statement. In addition to profit on actual sales, the figure of $58.3 also includes the anticipated profit on the units produced for inventory and the intracompany profit on the interdepartmental transfers. Profit on the inventory buildup, using the data on page 99, is equal to

$$[.080\ .104] \cdot \begin{bmatrix} 100 \\ 100 \end{bmatrix} = \$18.40.$$

Profit on interdepartmental transfers is given as

$$[.080\ .104] \cdot [X - B]$$

$$= [.080\ .104] \cdot \begin{bmatrix} (238.9 - 200) \\ (376.4 - 300) \end{bmatrix}$$

$$= [.080\ .104] \cdot \begin{bmatrix} 38.9 \\ 76.4 \end{bmatrix} = \$11.10.$$

Profit as shown on the income statement, again using the data from page 99, can be computed as follows:

$$[.080\ .104] \cdot \begin{bmatrix} 100 \\ 200 \end{bmatrix} = \$28.80.$$

This amount can also be determined by eliminating both types of unallowable profit from the total amount. Specifically, we have

accounting profit $= \$58.30 - \$18.40 - \$11.10 = \$28.80$.

This example should illustrate some of the many ways that input-output analysis can be useful in the area of financial planning in situations where the necessary assumptions are not unduly restrictive. It should also illustrate that the techniques of input-output analysis are easily managed once the fundamentals of matrix mathematics have been mastered. We will turn now to an illustration of the financial planning uses of the Markov-chain models from Chapter 4.

3. FINANCIAL PLANNING USES OF THE ACCOUNTS-RECEIVABLE VALUATION MODEL

Although we emphasized only the valuation aspects of Markov-chain models in Chapter 4, such models really have much broader potential applicability in accounting. In this section and the following one we illustrate that they can be helpful in approaching many of the important decisions related to managing assets, as well as to valuing them.

With respect to accounts receivable, a forecast of future collections and write-offs each period, based on some sales forecast, is very important in cash budgeting, in estimating manpower requirements for the collection and payment processes, and in judging the appropriateness of current credit policies. We will show that the accounts receivable model in Chapter 4 can be used to make such a forecast of collections and write-offs. Using the same numerical example as in that chapter, we will illustrate the technique and show its relevance to the budgeting, manning, and credit-terms decisions.

If new credit sales are generated at a rate equal to d dollars each period, it can be shown that a Markovian accounts receivable process eventually approaches a "steady state" in which the distribution of dollars in the various age categories no longer changes from period to period. This steady-state distribution $B*$ can be expressed as

$$B* = D[I - Q]^{-1}, \tag{1}$$

where D is the row vector $[d, 0, 0]$, and Q is the transient-to-transient partition of the transition matrix.

Actually, it is also possible to treat "steady state" behavior of processes which involve seasonal variability in sales and those which exhibit sales growth over time. These situations involve much more complicated calculations, however, and they require a more flexible interpretation of what is meant by a "steady state." We will concentrate here, therefore, on the "constant sales" case for purposes of illustration. Reference (1) at the end of the chapter deals with the more complicated cases.

If we assume that new sales each month are $1,000,000, Eq. (1) would indicate an eventual steady-state accounts-receivable distribution of $[1,000,000 \quad 840,000 \quad 237,000]$ calculated as follows:

$$D = [1,000,000 \quad 0 \quad 0],$$

$$[I - Q]^{-1} = \begin{bmatrix} 1 & .84 & .237 \\ 0 & 1.67 & .475 \\ 0 & 0 & 1.43 \end{bmatrix},$$

$$B^* = D \cdot [I - Q]^{-1} = [1,000,000 \quad 0 \quad 0] \cdot \begin{bmatrix} 1 & .84 & .237 \\ 0 & 1.67 & .475 \\ 0 & 0 & 1.43 \end{bmatrix}$$

$$= [1,000,000 \quad 840,000 \quad 237,000].$$

To verify that this is really a steady-state condition, notice what happens when we multiply B^* times Q. The result will be the expected age distribution one period hence. With allowances for rounding, we have

$$B^* \cdot Q = [1,000,000 \quad 840,000 \quad 237,000] \cdot \begin{bmatrix} 0 & .5 & 0 \\ 0 & .4 & .2 \\ 0 & 0 & .3 \end{bmatrix}$$

$$= [0 \quad 840,000 \quad 237,000].$$

Thus once we reach the point at which the age distribution is given by B^*, the next transition, including the $1,000,000 of new sales, will still show an age distribution equal to B^*.

It is interesting to note that the actual distribution vector B which exists at the time we are making the future steady-state projection is irrelevant in the calculation. This may seem strange until you realize that it will take many periods for the process to approach the steady state. All the dollars represented in the current vector will have been absorbed as either a collection or a write-off in the intervening periods and will thus not be a factor in determining the steady-state condition. In other words, by the time the steady-state condition is approached, the effect of the $1,000,000 per period of new sales dominates any carry-over effect from the initial distribution vector.

Once the steady state is approached, absorptions will also be constant from period to period. Specifically, they will be given by $B^* \cdot R$, where R is the transient-to-absorbing partition of the transition matrix. For the example at hand, and allowing for roundings, we have

$$B^* \cdot R = [1,000,000 \quad 840,000 \quad 237,000] \cdot \begin{bmatrix} .5 & 0 \\ .4 & 0 \\ .5 & .2 \end{bmatrix}$$

$$= [953,000 \quad 47,000].$$

You will note that the two elements of $B^* \cdot R$ must sum to $1,000,000, because $1,000,000 is being added to the process each period and the dollars tied up in the intervening stages are holding constant. It is this $B^* \cdot R$ vector which is very useful in analyzing cash budgeting, manpower scheduling, and credit-policy decisions.

With respect to cash budgeting, this vector tells us that the steady-state condition involves $953,000 of cash collections per period. This is the basic inflow data around which a long-range cash budget can be built. If the average size of an individual payment is $50, this figure further tells us that we must be prepared to process about 19,000 payments each period in the long run. If one clerk can process 5000 payments per month, we need to be thinking in terms of a four-person staff for this function. With respect to credit policy, the relationship of $47,000 in write-offs to $953,000 in collections each period provides a check on the adequacy of our controls over credit approval and follow-up. Is 5% (47,000/953,000) an acceptable number? If management feels it is, current credit policies can be maintained. If it is too high or too low, management can, respectively, tighten or loosen them. It should be noted that this analysis assumes that the level of sales would not be affected by changes in credit policy. Our purpose is only to illustrate very broadly how the model can be useful in decision-making, not to offer carefully constructed decision rules.

The vector B^* itself can probably also be of some use in estimating the manpower requirements of the collections function. Assume, for example, that an average of 10 minutes per month is spent following up 30 to 60-day-old accounts and 20 minutes per month in following up 60 to 90-day-old accounts. Assume also that the average account balance is $200. With these assumptions, we can calculate the long-run manpower requirements of our collection effort as follows:

30 to 60-day-old accounts
$840,000 ÷ $200 = 4200 accounts,
4200 accounts × $\frac{1}{6}$ hour per month = 700 hours per month.

60 to 90-day-old accounts
$237,000 ÷ $200 = 1185 accounts,
1185 accounts × $\frac{1}{3}$ hour per month = 395 hours per month
Total collection effort required = 1095 hours per month

If each clerk works 175 hours per month, the above effort will require about six full-time people in the long run.

None of these potential managerial uses of the Markov-chain model have been explored very fully because the intent in this book is only to introduce the concept of matrix mathematics as a relevant analytic tool. As you begin to apply the tool in more complex managerial decision-making situations, you will have to be much more careful in stating assumptions and interpreting results. In many situations, however, you may find the matrix approach very helpful. Let us turn now to the inventory-valuation model from Chapter 4 and consider its uses in financial planning.

4. FINANCIAL PLANNING USES OF THE INVENTORY VALUATION MODEL

In this section we consider two decision-oriented questions similar to those treated in the accounts receivable example. Specifically:

1. If we purchase 10,000 units of raw material each period, what is the maximum number of units we will have available to sell each month in the long run?
2. What are the long-run manpower requirements for the inspection function under this purchasing assumption?

Both of these questions focus on the managerial implications of the "steady-state" distribution vector we considered in the preceding section. We will also consider using the inventory model to construct a long-run cash budget for the firm.

You will remember from the preceding section that the steady-state distribution vector B^* is given by the expression

$$B^* = D \cdot [I - Q]^{-1}.$$

In answering question (1) above, we can calculate B^* as follows:

$$D = [10,000 \quad 0 \quad 0],$$

$$[I - Q]^{-1} = \begin{bmatrix} 2 & 1.6 & .62 \\ 0 & 2 & .88 \\ 0 & 0 & 1.1 \end{bmatrix},$$

$$B^* = D \cdot [I - Q]^{-1} = [10{,}000 \quad 0 \quad 0] \cdot \begin{bmatrix} 2 & 1.6 & .62 \\ 0 & 2 & .78 \\ 0 & 0 & 1.1 \end{bmatrix}$$

$$= [20{,}000 \quad 16{,}000 \quad 6{,}200].$$

You can satisfy yourself that this really represents a steady-state condition by verifying that $[B^* \cdot Q] + D = B^*$. Specifically, we have

$$Q = \begin{bmatrix} .5 & .4 & 0 \\ 0 & .5 & .35 \\ 0 & 0 & .1 \end{bmatrix},$$

$$[B^* \cdot Q] + D = [20{,}000 \quad 16{,}000 \quad 6{,}200] \cdot \begin{bmatrix} .5 & .4 & 0 \\ 0 & .5 & .35 \\ 0 & 0 & .1 \end{bmatrix} + [10{,}000 \quad 0 \quad 0]$$

$$= [10{,}000 \quad 16{,}000 \quad 6{,}200] + [10{,}000 \quad 0 \quad 0]$$

$$= [20{,}000 \quad 16{,}000 \quad 6{,}200]$$

$$= B^*.$$

We noted in the preceding section that once this steady state is approached, absorptions will stabilize at a monthly rate of $B^* \cdot R$. For the present example, this result is

$$B^* \cdot R = [20{,}000 \quad 16{,}000 \quad 6{,}200] \cdot \begin{bmatrix} 0 & .1 \\ 0 & .15 \\ .85 & .05 \end{bmatrix} = [5{,}270 \quad 4{,}730].$$

In answer to question (1), therefore, only 5,270 units will be available for sale each month in the long run, although 10,000 are put into production. Note that this analysis could also be turned around to compute the necessary raw-material input to support a desired level of long-run sales.

We will postpone answering question (2) until we have constructed the long-run cash budget. The reason for this postponement will become apparent at that time. For purposes of the cash budget, we will assume that all the flows represented in Table 4.6 are realized in cash each period. A more complicated example might couple the Markov inventory process, with a Markov collection process, but we will not depart from a simple cash expenses—cash sales assumption here.

As a first step in developing a steady-state cash budget we construct a matrix M (Table 5.2) which arrays the expected number of transitions from the three transient states to each of the transient and absorbing states in any period; the initial B vector is given by $[20,000\ 16,000\ 6,200]$. The ijth entry of M represents the product of the ith element of B multiplied by the probability P_{ij} from the transition matrix shown in Table 4.5.

Table 5.2   Expected transitions matrix M

To From	Raw material	Semi- finished	Finished	Sold	Scrapped	Total
Raw material	10,000	8,000	0	0	2,000	20,000
Semi-finished	0	8,000	5,600	0	2,400	16,000
Finished	0	0	620	5,270	310	6,200

The next step is to multiply each element of M by the corresponding element of C. We will summarize the results for each row of M and keep track of the multiplication in terms of the cost-category breakdown shown in Table 4.5. The result is a cash flow-summary like that shown in Table 5.3.

Expected collections each period will in the long run be 5,270 × $85 or $448,000, to the nearest $100. We can thus summarize the overall expected monthly flows as follows.

Collections		$448,000
Disbursements		
Purchases	$100,000	
Finishing	140,000	
Inspection	94,300	
Semi-finishing	40,000	
Storage	32,200	
Scrap	32,900	439,400
Net change in cash	+	$ 8,600

Since we assumed that there are no accruals, this statement is also the projected long-run monthly earnings statement. You may be surprised by the rather slim operating margin (less than 2% sales). One benefit

Table 5.3.   Cash-flow summary

Expense categories*	Purchases	Storage	Semi-finishing	Finishing	Inspection	Scrap	Total
Number of units							
New purchases (10,000)	100,000	0	0	0	0	0	100,000
Raw material (20,000)	0	18,000	40,000	0	40,000	14,000	112,000
Semi-finished (16,000)	0	13,600	0	140,000	32,000	16,800	202,400
Finished (6,200)	0	600	0	0	22,300	2,100	25,000
Total	100,000	32,220	40,000	140,000	94,300	32,900	439,400

*All entries rounded to the nearest $100.

of preparing such projections is to show the overall impact of a set of assumptions and relationships. In the case at hand, it was not clear that the business was such a marginal one until all the factors were tied together in the form of a long-run cash (and earnings) budget.

Returning to the inspection manpower question raised initially, the easiest approach is to use the cash budget. A monthly outlay of $94,300 represents, 23,575 inspections, since the cost per inspection is $4.00. If we assume that this per-unit cost is made up of $\frac{1}{3}$ hour at $9.00 per hour and $1.00 of materials and supplies, the 23,575 inspections represent about 7,860 manhours per month. At 175 hours per employee per month, we will require a work force of about 45 inspectors.

As in the preceding section, we won't pursue any of these potential planning uses of the inventory model beyond the introductory stage. The purpose is to consider what kinds of problems can be usefully attacked by the model, rather than to explore any one problem in depth.

SELECTED REFERENCES

1. Cyert, R. M., H. J. Davidson, and G. L. Thompson. "Estimation of the Allowance for Doubtful Accounts by Markov Chains," *Management Science*, April 1962.
2. Farag, Shawki M. "A Planning Model for the Divisionalized Enterprise," *The Accounting Review*, April 1968.
3. Gambling, Trevor. "A Technological Model for Use in Input-Output Analysis and Cost Accounting," *Management Accounting*, December 1968.
4. Gambling, Trevor, and Ahmed Nour. "A Note on Input-Output Analysis: Its Uses in Macro-Economics and Micro-Economics," *The Accounting Review*, January 1970.
5. Ijiri, Yuji. "An Application of Input-Output Analysis to Some Problems in Cost Accounting," *Management Accounting*, April 1968.
6. Livingstone, John Leslie. "Input-Output Analysis for Cost Accounting, Planning and Control," *The Accounting Review*, January 1969.
7. Richards, Allen B. "Input-Output Accounting for Business," *The Accounting Review*, July 1960.

INDEX

INDEX

THE AUTHOR

Professor John K. Shank, of the Harvard Business School, earned the A.B. degree from Oberlin College, the M.B.A. degree from the University of Pittsburgh, and the Ph.D. degree in Accounting from The Ohio State University. He also holds a C.P.A. certificate and is a member of the American Institute of C.P.A.'s. Before joining the Business School Faculty, he taught at The Ohio State University for three years and was associated with the national consulting accountancy firm of Touche Ross and Company for three years. He has also been involved in consulting projects and management education seminars with such companies as General Electric, The Mead Corporation, Coca-Cola, National Cash Register, and Johnson & Johnson.

Professor Shank's current research interests include the linkage between corporate planning and budgeting systems, the diffusion of innovations in corporate financial reporting practices, and the development of new models for minority economic development.

THE ADDISON-WESLEY PAPERBACK SERIES IN ACCOUNTING
William J. Bruns, Jr., Editor

MANAGEMENT ACCOUNTING AND BEHAVIORAL SCIENCE
By **Edwin H. Caplan,** University of New Mexico

134 pp, paperbound (1971)

INFORMATION ANALYSIS
By **Joel S. Demski,** Stanford University   In press (1972)

COMPARATIVE ACCOUNTING THEORY
By **Daniel L. McDonald,** University of Washington   In press (1972)

ADDISON-WESLEY PUBLISHING COMPANY
Reading, Massachusetts · Menlo Park, California · London · Don Mills, Ontario